The
Bulbous Plants
OF TURKEY

The
Bulbous Plants
OF TURKEY

An illustrated guide to
the bulbous petaloid monocotyledons
of Turkey

Amaryllidaceae · Iridaceae · Liliaceae

TURHAN BAYTOP
University of Istanbul
and
BRIAN MATHEW
Royal Botanic Gardens, Kew

B. T. Batsford Ltd. London
in association with the
Alpine Garden Society

We dedicate this book to
the botanists and naturalists of the last century
who travelled under difficult conditions
in search of plants in Turkey.

The figure on the title page
is reputed to represent *Iris persica*.
It is taken from a small ivory Hittite plate
(height 3 cm) of the thirteenth century BC
which is housed in the Museum of
Anatolian Civilizations, Ankara.

Turhan Baytop is Professor of Pharmcognosy at Istanbul University.
He has been studying the bulbous plants of Turkey for more than
30 years and is the collector of many newly described species.

Brian Mathew is a Principal Scientific Officer at the Royal Botanic
gardens, Kew. He is the author of *The Iris*, *The Crocus*, *Dwarf Bulbs*
and *The Larger Bulbs*, all published by Batsford.

© Turhan Baytop and Brian Mathew 1984
First published 1984

ISBN 0 7134 4517 3

Printed in Great Britain by
Butler & Tanner Ltd,
Frome and London
for the Publisher,
B. T. Batsford Ltd
4 Fitzhardinge Street
London W1H 0AH

CONTENTS

ÇİÇEKLERİN DİLİ

Çiğdem der ki ben elâyım,
Yiğit başına belâyım.
Hepinizden ben âlâyım,
Benden âlâ çiçek varmı?

Al baharlı mavi dağlar,
Yarim gurbet elde ağlar.

Lâle der ki behey Tanrı,
Neden benim boynum eğri.
Yardan ayri düştüm gayri,
Benden âlâ çiçek varmı?

Çayır çimen dolu dağlar,
Yarim gurbet elde ağlar.

Nevruz der ki ben nazlıyım,
Sarp kayalarda gizliyim.
Mavi donlu gök gözlüyüm,
Benden âlâ çiçek varmı?

Al baharlı mavi dağlar,
Yarim gurbet elde ağlar.

Sümbül der ki boynum uzun,
Yapraklarım düzüm düzüm.
Beni ak gerdana dizin,
Benden âlâ çiçek varmı?

Çayır çimen dolu dağlar,
Yarim gurbet elde ağlar.

(Şarkışla'dan bir halk türküsü)

THE LANGUAGE OF FLOWERS

The Crocus says: I am bluish,
I am the brave's sweet burden,
I am the fairest of all you,
Is there a flower better than me?

Scarlet spring on blue mountains,
My lover weeps away from me.

The Tulip says: O praised God,
Why is my neck bent down?
I fell apart from my lover,
Is there a flower better than me?

Grass and meadow covered the mountains,
My lover weeps away from me.

The Iris says: I am gracious,
I am hidden in the steep rocks,
Dressed in blue and my eyes also blue,
Is there a flower better than me?

Scarlet spring on blue mountains,
My lover weeps away from me.

The Hyacinth says: My neck is long,
And my leaves are well ranged.
String me around the white neck,
Is there a flower better than me?

Grass and meadow covered the mountains,
My lover weeps away from me.

(An old Turkish popular song from Şarkışla,
a town near Konya)

PREFACE

The countries of the Near East, and especially Turkey, are the homes of many beautiful bulbous plants, some of which have been cultivated in European gardens for several centuries. Species which are associated with this region include well-known classical plants such as *Hyacinthus orientalis*, *Lilium candidum*, *Tulipa clusiana*, *Narcissus tazetta*, *Sternbergia lutea*, *Crocus sativus* and *Iris persica*. In fact some of these bulbs are still, as in former times, dug up in the wild for export to other countries.

The interest in the flora of Asia Minor is very old and many books and papers have been published on the subject. There is, however, no publication dealing solely with the bulbous plants of Turkey and it has been our aim to produce a useful guide, with colour photographs showing the great range of attractive species which occur there. Short descriptions and distributions are given, and the references to each species, so that the reader can check the original descriptions if necessary.

The term 'bulbous' is a very loose one and, for the purpose of this book, has been taken to mean any monocotyledonous plant which has a swollen storage organ enabling it to survive an adverse climatic period such as a long, dry summer. Thus, one will find in this book not only plants possessing true bulbs such as *Narcissus*, *Sternbergia* and *Muscari*, but also corms like *Crocus* and *Gladiolus*, and rhizomes such as *Iris*. In order to restrict the size of the book in some way we have taken into account only the three most important families, namely *Amaryllidaceae*, *Iridaceae* and *Liliaceae*. We have also only dealt with the native members of these three families although there are some exotic species which are cultivated to some extent.

The petaloid monocotyledons of Turkey are still not well-known. Many species flower in the very early spring, when the roads are very bad, or in the autumn when there are few travellers to collect and observe them. Some regions are almost unknown as far as the bulbous plants are concerned. During the last ten years our knowledge of these plants has greatly increased and several new species have been described, as well as many new distribution records. There is however a vast amount of work to be done on the distribution and ecology of each species.

It is very likely that more species will be recorded for the flora of Turkey in the future as botanical exploration continues, especially in the areas bordering other species-rich countries such as the Caucasus, Iran and Syria. Recent examples of new records are *Colchicum macrophyllum* (in Rhodes, now known from Muğla), *Iris urmiensis* (in Iran, now found in Hakkâri), *Fritillaria stribrnyi* (in Bulgaria, now found in European Turkey),

Galanthus graecus (in Greece, now known from S.W. Turkey), *Sternbergia sicula* (in Greece, now recorded in W. Turkey).

The book is based mainly on the knowledge and material gathered by the authors on their many collecting trips made since 1965. The herbarium specimens from these excursions are deposited at Kew, Edinburgh, and Istanbul University, Faculty of Pharmacy.

Taxonomy and Nomenclature   We have not set out to make this an authoritative work on the monocotyledons of Turkey. Only a great deal of research and time can produce such results. The superb work of Dr P. H. Davis, *The Flora of Turkey*, will shortly be nearing completion when the final volume of monocotyledons is published. Undoubtedly there will be some different concepts of the taxa involved, inevitable name changes and some new species described. Author abbreviations follow R. D. Meikle, *Draft Index of Author Abbreviations*, H.M.S.O. (1980).

Illustrations   The colour plates are reproductions of photographs taken by the authors of plants either growing in the wild in Turkey or of Turkish origin and cultivated in our gardens.

Distribution   For most of the species mentioned the distribution is given by the number of the region (see map, page 18). Endemics are indicated, and for non-endemic species an idea of the total area of distribution is given. For conservation purposes no very precise localities are given.

Literature   It is impossible to give all the references to Turkish bulbous plants and we have selected only the most important or most interesting (see page 119).

Vernacular Names   Unfortunately there is not a local Turkish name for every species. Sometimes there are several different names for one species, and sometimes only one name for all the species in one genus. For example, *Çiğdem* is the name for all *Crocus* species regardless of flower colour or flowering period. *Zambak* can refer to *Iris* or *Lilium* depending upon the region.

Turkish people are very fond of the early bulbous plants and they figure very prominently in local place names, in songs and in folk lore. Some mountains and villages are named after them, for example Sümbül Dağ (Hyacinth mountain) near Hakkâri, Lâleli (Place of the Tulips) near Erzurum, Lâleli geçidi (Tulip pass) between Kayseri and Sivas, Çiğdemli (Place of the Crocus) near Erzurum, Soğanli Dağ (Mountain of the bulbs) near Kayseri, and Soğanli Dağlari between Rize and Erzurum.

Some local Turkish plant names have very precise meanings which are not at all obvious to outsiders. Take for example *Colchicum speciosum*, normally known as *Acı çiğdem*. In the north-east of the country it is called *Var git* which means 'go away'. Its autumnal flowers tell the country people that it is time to leave their alpine meadows, or *yaylas*, and return to the comfort of the villages. In western Turkey the late flowering *Colchicum variegatum* has a special significance for hunters. After the time of its flowering it is hard to find the *Keklik*, or partridge, since it flies southwards. *Morca*, the name for *C. variegatum*, appears in the saying '*Morca kekligi vurmak zorca*', or 'Hunting partridges is now difficult'.

Crocuses, Irises, Tulips and Fritillaries are often mentioned in Turkish songs.

We have recorded the vernacular names of many species in our travels in Turkey and they are given in the text, and in the Turkish Index.

Turkish Summary For those Turkish readers who are interested in these plants there is a summary at the end in the Turkish language. However, we hope that in the future there might be sufficient interest to produce a Turkish edition.

ACKNOWLEDGEMENTS

We would like to offer our grateful thanks to the Directors of the Royal Botanic Gardens Kew and Edinburgh, and of the Pharmaceutical Botany Department at Istanbul University, for the use of their herbarium material. We also thank the numerous people who have contributed information or have collected bulbous plants in Turkey, thus adding to the fund of knowledge available to us. Especially valuable has been the taxonomic work by the authors of the accounts of genera prepared for *The Flora of Turkey*, under the direction of Dr P. H. Davis who has personally collected an enormous quantity of material and information in Turkey. In connection with Volume 8 of the *Flora*, which includes the bulbous plants, we gratefully acknowledge the work by C. D. Brickell, J. Cullen, P. H. Davis, A. P. Hamilton, F. Kollmann, M. Koyuncu, W. Marais, R. R. Mill, E. V. Mordak, N. Özhatay, K. Persson, E. M. Rix, Kit Tan and the late Per Wendelbo.

We have, in a later part of this book, given biographical notes concerning collectors and botanists of the past who have made major contributions to the general knowledge of the bulbs of Turkey but there are of course also many modern collectors to whom we are equally indebted. To list them all by name would be impossible since everyone who has recorded or collected specimens of bulbs in Turkey has provided helpful background knowledge. We would however like to acknowledge the work done by Mr E. K. Balls whose excellent collections of herbarium material, made in Anatolia between 1933 and 1935, have been the source of much information. Our thanks also go to Mr A. Atilla of Istanbul, past Director of the Istanbul Botanic Garden, who has made many excursions in Turkey, mainly to collect bulbous plants. Of the numerous others we must mention A. Aksoy, the late John Allison, P. Ball, Sir Colville Barclay, M. Baron, A. Baytop, H. and M. Crook, H. Demiriz, the late P. Furse, A. Güner, the late S. V. Horton, M. A. T. Johnson, H. J. Leep, J. R. Marr, T. Norman, R. D. Nutt, E. Pasche, O. Sønderhousen, N. J. Stevens, the late A. J. Tomlinson, and J. M. Watson. For typing the manuscript we would like to thank Maggie Mathew.

Finally we owe many thanks to Seyit Ünsal, driver at the Faculty of Pharmacy, Istanbul University; his skill in taking us safely to many remote spots in Anatolia has undoubtedly assisted greatly in our work.

LIST OF ILLUSTRATIONS

The colour photographs were mostly taken by the authors in the Turkish countryside, except for a few which show plants in cultivation. The photographs of *Bellevalia pycnantha*, *Fritillaria latifolia* and *Lilium szovitsianum* var. *armenum* were taken by Paul Furse, those of *Iris gatesii*, *I. histrio* and *I. aucheri* were by Adil Güner, and *Fritillaria crassifolia* subsp. *kurdica* was photographed by Helen Tomlinson.

Colour photographs (between pages 68 and 69)

Black and white photographs

ONE

History

Asia Minor, the home of deities[37], is also the home of many bulbous plants. The Hittites who lived in this region in about 2000 B.C. used to grow bulbous plants like onion, garlic, leek and saffron. They celebrated the arrival of spring, as the snow melted away on the plateaux of Anatolia and the flowers began to appear, by holding Spring Festivals.

M. S. Ar gives us the following information on the names of the spring festivals of the Hittites: 'We know for a certainty that the names of the festivals are *Puruliyaş* and *An.tah.şum-sar*. We have no idea what the former means, but it is certain that the meaning of the latter is bulb. This word is originally Sumerian, and the suffix "sar" is enough evidence to show that it signifies a certain plant.'[7]

Şum-sar and *Şum.sikil-sar*, observes H. Ertem, are the names the Hittites gave to garlic and onion respectively.[50] The above information enables us to connect *An.tah.şum-sar* with a bulbous plant which blooms in spring. We believe that this plant whose flowers ornament the Anatolian plateaux in the early spring is the Crocus for, to this day, people in Anatolia welcome the blooming of the crocuses on the plateaux, because it heralds the end of winter. It is reasonable to assume that the name of one of the spring festivals of the Hittites was 'Crocus Festival'.

The coming of spring is still celebrated in Turkey on 6 May under the name *Hıdrellez* (Spring-feast) and on this date people go for picnics. In some areas (Adana, Diyarbakır, Gaziantep, Refahiye, etc.) a special pilav (*Çiğdem pilavı* = Crocus pilav), prepared with *bulgur* (cracked wheat) and *çiğdem* (Crocus) bulbs, is eaten at Hıdrellez.

Floriculture was at its height during the rule of the Ottomans. In the Sûrnâme of Murat III (1582), which described the 52-day long circumcision feasts of Prince Mehmed, the son of Sultan Murat III, the miniatures in the chapters on florists are of great significance in that they indicate the level which floriculture in Istanbul had reached by the end of the sixteenth century.[148]

According to the famous Turkish traveller Evliya Çelebi, in the 1630s there were about 80 flower-shops and 300 florists in Istanbul which was also rich in vineyards and orchards. The gardens of the villas and waterside residences on the Bosphorus were decorated with tulips and hyacinths. He remarks: '*Lâlezar* (Tulipbed) Excursion Spot: The various kinds of the tulip widely known as the *Kağithane* tulip are found here. One is intoxicated at the sight of this spot in the tulip season.'[51]

The most important decorative design between the sixteenth and the eighteenth centuries was that based on the flower. This decorated metal objects, fabrics, book covers, woodwork, glass-ware, tiles, carpets, etc. Among these flower designs, the most frequently seen were those of carnations, roses, tulips, hyacinths and jonquils.[45,134,135]

In Istanbul, during the Ottoman Period, bulbous plants were held in the highest esteem. Not taking roses and carnations into consideration, it can be said that for a number of centuries the various forms of tulips, hyacinths, jonquils, ranunculus, anemones and irises were the chief ornamental flowers of the orchards and gardens of Istanbul.[134,135]

There is clear evidence also that wild flower bulbs were brought from various regions of the Ottoman Empire to the palace gardens of Istanbul. There is an order by Sultan Murat III, written in 1593 to the Governor General of Maraş, in which he issues instructions for the collection from the mountains of his district of 50,000 bulbs of white *Hyacinthus* (*ak sümbül*) and 50,000 of the blue form (*gök sümbül*) for urgent dispatch to Istanbul. (From A. R. Altinay, *Life in Istanbul in the XIth Hegira century* (in Turkish), Istanbul, 1930.)

The home of the tulip, a very important decorative flower during the seventeenth and eighteenth centuries, is said to be Central Asia[72], but about 20 types of wild tulips also occur in Anatolia.[68] In addition to these it is certain that a number of tulip bulbs were brought from Central Asia to Persia, Anatolia and even to Europe by the Turks during the Turkish migrations.

Tulip designs which are found on tiles excavated from the Konya Alaeddin Hill and on the ceiling ornaments of the Alaeddin Palace in Konya point to the fact that this flower design was introduced by the Anatolian Seljuks in the twelfth century and has been used ever since.

During the reign of the Ottomans, the tulip was the symbol of the Ottoman Palace, just as the lily was of the Princes of Western Europe.

Celâleddin Rûmi (Mevlânâ) (1207–1273) was the first Anatolian poet to write about tulips.[134]

The fact that no tulip design is found on the buildings, coins and works of art of the Byzantines proves that the tulip was of no value before the Turkish invasion. It was obviously the Turks who brought the tulip to Istanbul since tulip designs are found on some of the buildings and fountains which were constructed soon after the Turkish invasion.

Şeyh Mehmed Lâlezari[82] gives us the following description of the Istanbul Tulip, which was obtained as a result of selection over a period of many centuries. The flowers are almond-shaped, the tepals are dagger-shaped and the tips are pointed. In the Ottoman Period, the only tulips that were valuable were those with the above features. In order to obtain new forms, the seeds of the cross-bred tulips were sown, and the resulting flowers which appeared after three to 12 years were evaluated by a Committee of Specialists called *Ser Şeküfeciyan-ı Hassa*. In the evaluation, the appearance of the flower, its shape, its colour, the shape of the stamens, etc. were separately judged. The tulips that the specialists considered perfect were given awards, and their owners were given certificates. The new forms, to which the poets dedicated couplets, were given names. These names were mostly in Arabic or Persian, such as *Nize-i rummâni*, *Şive-engiz*, *Ferah-efza*, *Zevk-bahs*, *Ruh-perver*, but there were also some Turkish ones mental five-volume work *Flora Orientalis*, 1867–1884; more than 80 species of Turkish bulbous plants were described as new by him. The Boissier herbarium is housed at Geneva but duplicates of his specimens are to be found in many other European herbaria.

Species named in honour of E. Boissier: *Colchicum boissieri*; *Crocus boissieri*.

Biogr. and bibliogr.: Christ, H.: Notice sur la vie et les travaux botaniques d'Edmond Boissier in *Flora Orientalis*, supplementum 1, Genève & Bâle, 1888; Hochreutiner, B. P. G.: Les collections d'Edmond Boissier à l'Herbier Boissier in *Boissiera* 3: 225 (1938).

Joseph Friedrich Nicolaus Bornmüller

Born 6 December 1862 in Hildburghausen (Turingen); died 19 December 1948 in Weimar. German botanist, curator of the Belgrade Botanic Garden (1887–89), and keeper of the Herbarium Haussknecht from 1903 in Weimar (now moved to Jena).

He travelled widely and collected a great deal of material in the Balkans, Turkey, Iran, Syria and Palestine. Specimens from his collections are widely distributed throughout the major European herbaria but the important material in Berlin was partly destroyed by air raids on 1 March 1943.

His Anatolian expeditions were as follows: 1889–90: N. Anatolia (Amasya); 1892–93: Central and E. Anatolia; 1899: Central Anatolia and Bursa; 1906: W. Anatolia (Izmir, Yamanlar Dağ, Ikikardeş Dağ, Menemen, Tahtali Dağ, etc.); 1929: Central and N. Anatolia.

He published more than 30 papers on the flora of Turkey, for example, 'Symbolae ad Floram Anatoliam', Part 1 in *Fedde, Repert. Spec. Nov.* Beih. 89: 1 (1936); Part 2, loc. cit. 89: 65 (1936); Part 3, loc. cit. 89: 117 (1938); Part 4/5, loc. cit. 89: 165 (1940); Part 6, loc. cit. 89: 261 (1941); Part 7/8, loc. cit. 89: 309 (1944).

Turkish bulbous plants described by J. Bornmüller include *Allium asclepiadeum*, *A. trilophostemon*, *Fritillaria straussii*, *Iris melanosticta*, *Merendera kurdica*.

Species named in honour of J. Bornmüller: *Colchicum bornmuelleri*.

Biogr. and bibliogr.: Schwarz, O.: Zu Joseph Bornmüllers fünfundsiebzigstem Geburstage, Bornmüller-Festschrift, in *Fedde, Repert. Spec. Nov.* Beih. 100: 1 (1938); Wiśniewski, T.: Verzeichnis der von J. Bornmüller verfassten Arbeiten in *Fedde, Repert. Spec. Nov.* Beih, 100: 11 (1938); Wagenitz, G.: Joseph Bornmüller (1862–1948) in *Willdenowia* 3, 2: 343 (1962).

Ogier Ghislain de Busbecq

Born 1522 in Comines (Flanders); died 28 October 1592 at St Germain (Rouen, France). Flemish diplomat, ambassador of the Emperor Ferdinand I in Constantinople. He entered the service of Ferdinand of Austria, and was sent by him to the court of Suleiman the Magnificent in 1554 and again in 1556. He returned after six years to Vienna in 1562. He travelled from Istanbul to Amasya, via Izmit, Iznik, Bozüyük and Ankara; during these travels he discovered the *Monumentum Ancyranum* and gathered together in Istanbul many Greek manuscripts, coins and inscriptions.

Busbecq also has the honour of introducing the garden Tulip into Europe from Istanbul. The first of these Tulips to be grown outside Turkey was named, by Conrad Gesner in 1559, *Tulipa turcarum*.

Plants named in honour of O. G. de Busbecq include genus *Busbecquia* (*Hyacinthus*).

Biogr. and bibliogr.: Forster, E. S.: *The Turkish letters of Ogier Ghiselin de Busbecq*, Oxford, 1968; Huussen, A. H.: *Het leven van Ogier Ghislain de Busbecq*, Leiden, 1949.

Mrs C. G. Danford

Little is known of Mrs Danford other than that she travelled in the late nineteenth century in Turkey with her husband who was a keen ornithologist. In 1890 he was the British Consul in Transsylvania, Roumania.

Mrs Danford collected plants and sent material to J. G. Baker at Kew, and to George Maw. The former described *Iris danfordiae* in her honour. The latter named *Crocus danfordiae* for her and in fact dedicated the whole of his fabulous work *A monograph of the genus Crocus*, London, 1886, to Mr and Mrs Danford. The dedication by Maw is worth repeating for it emphasises the importance of their work: 'The journeys of Mr and Mrs Danford throughout the length and breadth of Asia Minor in the years 1876, 1878 and 1879 added much to the knowledge of the distribution of Crocuses in that district. Many of the vignettes appearing in the present book have been engraved from original sketches made by Mr Danford in the remote region of the Taurus and other parts of Asia Minor, and to Mrs Danford I am indebted for the roots of several new species of Crocus discovered by her, and also for much valuable information respecting the habitats of Crocuses throughout Asia Minor.'

In England, the Danfords lived at Ayres End, Harpenden.

Georg Egger

German consul in the town of Tabriz in N.W. Iran. He was keen on hunting and on the local flora and made many excursions collecting bulbous plants, many of which were sent to the firm of van Tubergen in Holland.

It is not clear to us if this is the same G. Egger who was a nurseryman in Jaffa. This Egger specialized in the bulbous plants of Asia Minor and may have owned another nursery in Syria since several labels on specimens at Kew bear the inscription 'G. Egger, Aleppo'. One Crocus, distributed as *C. tauri*, carries the label '*C. tauri*, Aleppo, Comm. G. Egger Jr., 17th Dec. 1912'. He offered for sale many native plants of the Cilician Taurus, such as *Eranthis cilicica*, *Iris tauri*, *Galanthus fosteri*, *Iris danfordiae* and *Sternbergia fischeriana*, so that we can be sure that he either travelled in Turkey himself or employed local people to collect for him.

Henry John Elwes

Born 16 May 1846; died 26 November 1922. Elwes was a wealthy English 'gentleman of leisure' with no particular profession, although he was in fact an extremely hard-working traveller who contributed much to our knowledge of plants, birds and insects, and took a special interest in forestry.

He was a very industrious traveller, journeying to Turkey, India, Sikkim, China, Tibet, Russia, Japan, Chile, Mexico, N. America and N. Africa, apart from almost every country in Europe. During these explorations he discovered and introduced many exciting plants including several Turkish species. Many of the plants which he collected were cultivated in his garden at Colesborne in Gloucestershire.

Elwes wrote a great deal about his researches, and the depth of his knowledge is displayed in such noteworthy works as *The Trees of Great Britain and Ireland*, 1906–1913, which runs to seven volumes; the impressive *Monograph of the genus Lilium*, 1880; *On the Geographical Distribution of Asiatic Birds*, 1880; and his autobiography, *Memoirs of Travel, Sport and Natural History*, 1930.

Some of his botanical specimens, which often formed the subjects for plates in *Curtis' Botanical Magazine*, are deposited in the Kew Herbarium.

Turkish species named in honour of H. J. Elwes: *Galanthus elwesii*, *Crocus elwesii*, *Fritillaria elwesii*.

Biogr. and bibliogr.: *Bot. Mag. Dedic.* 199 (1931); *Kew Bull.* 1923: 36 (1923); *Journ. Roy. Hort. Soc.* 49: 40 (1924).

Edward Forbes

Born Isle of Man, 2 February 1815; died 18 November 1854. British botanist, geologist and zoologist and great Manx naturalist. He started his career as a medical student and later joined the survey ship *Beacon* in the Mediterranean as a naturalist.

In 1842 he travelled in western Anatolia and made an important herbarium collection which is mainly deposited at Kew. He became Professor of Botany at King's College, London, and later held the Chair of Natural History at the University of Edinburgh. He published an account of his journey in Turkey, *Travels in Lycia, Milyas and the Cybiratis* (with Rev. E. T. Daniell and A. B. Spratt), London, 1847.

Species named in honour of E. Forbes: *Chionodoxa forbesii*, *Fritillaria forbesii*.

Biogr.: *Edward Forbes, a Centenary Tribute*, London Manx Society, 1915.

Caleb Frank Gates

Born 18 October 1857 in Chicago; died 9 April 1946 in Denver, Colorado. American instructor. President of Robert College of Istanbul (1903–32). He arrived in Mardin on 19 November 1881 as a missionary and was appointed Director of the High School of Mardin. He transferred to Harput on 9 October 1894, and became President of the Euphrates College. In 1903 he was elected President of the Robert College of Istanbul and resigned the Presidency in 1932, leaving on 26 June 1932 for America where he died at Denver, Colorado on 9 April 1946.

He was an ardent sportsman and was interested in the local flora of Mardin and Harput. He sent living material to Sir Michael Foster (*Iris bakeriana*, *I. gatesii*, etc.)

Species named in honour of C. F. Gates: *Iris gatesii*.

Biogr. and bibliogr.: *Encyclopédie Biographique de Turquie*, 102 (1928).

Heinrich Karl Haussknecht

Born 30 November 1838; died 7 July 1903 at Weimar. German botanist and Professor at the University of Weimar. He travelled widely in S. and E. Anatolia (the Taurus Mts., Gaziantep, Urfa, Mardin, Maraş, Kilis, Erzincan, Harput, Doğubeyazit, etc.) in 1865, 1867–8 and 1890. His specimens are represented in the herbaria of Geneva, Kew, Leningrad, Paris and especially Jena, where there is a Herbarium Haussknecht building.

Species named in honour of K. Haussknecht: *Crocus haussknechtii*, *Colchicum haussknechtii*.

Species described from Turkey by H. K. Haussknecht; *Allium phaneran-therum*, *Colchicum sieheanum*, *Fritillaria cilicico-taurica*, *F. sieheana*, *Muscari discolor*, *Ornithogalum persicum*.

Biogr. and bibliogr: *Mitt. Thür. Bot. Ver.*, new ser. 18: 1 (1903).

Karl Heinrich Emil Koch(C. (Carolus) Koch)

Born 6 June 1809 near Weimar; died 25 May 1879 in Berlin. A German botanist who studied medicine and natural sciences in Jena and Würzburg, and became Professor at the University of Berlin and Director of the Royal Botanic Garden, Berlin.

He travelled (1836–8, 1843–4) in the Caucasus, S. Russia and N.E. Anatolia (Trabzon, Rize, Ispir, Ardeşen, Hopa, Artvin, Ardahan, Erzurum, Muş, Malazgirt, Kağizman and Kars) and his specimens from these expeditions were deposited in Berlin; unfortunately the herbarium there was largely destroyed during the war and few of Koch's important collections have survived.

Koch published 'Beiträge zu einer Flora des Orientes' in *Linnaea* 21: 289 (1848); loc. cit. 22: 597 (1849); loc. cit. 23: 577 (1850); loc. cit. 24: 305 (1851).

New taxa described from N.E. Anatolia by C. Koch: *Crocus kotschyanus*, *C. suwarowianus*, *Gagea glacialis*, *Lilium ponticum*, *Ornithogalum gracilif-lorum*, *Scilla roseni*, *Tulipa julia*.

Biogr. and bibliogr.: Edmondson, J. R.: Turkish specimens from the herbarium of K. H. E. Koch (C. Koch) in *Taxon* 25: 256 (1976); Lack, H. W.: Karl Heinrich Emil Koch, IAPT-HI portraits No. 81 in *Taxon* 26: 385 (1977); Edmondson, J. R. and Lack, H. W.: The Turkish and Caucasian collection of C. Koch, I: Turkey, in *Notes R.B.G. Edinb.* 35: 321 (1977); Lack, H. W.: The Turkish and Caucasian collections of C. Koch, II: Caucasia, in *Notes R.B.G. Edinb.* 37: 79 (1978).

Theodor Kotschy

Born 13 April 1813 at Ustron (Silesia); died 11 June 1866 in Vienna. Austrian botanist and explorer. Adjunct keeper at the Botanisches Museum in Vienna. Travelled and collected in S. and W. Anatolia.

The collections of T. Kotschy are as follows: *Plantae in monte Tauro*, 1836 (Cilician Taurus); *Plantae Alep-Kurd-Mosul*, 1841 (Urfa, Siverek, Karacadağ, Diyarbakır, Mardin, Gaziantep, Nizip, Haran); *Iter Cilicicum*, 1853 (around Adana and Bolkar Dağ); *Cilicico-Kurdicum*, 1859 (Amanus mountains, Cilician Taurus, Gülek Boğazi, Bolkar Dağ, Bingöl Dağlari, Erzurum, Palandöken Dağlari, Bitlis, Muş, etc.); *Plantae Syriae bor. e monte Amano*, 1862 (Amanos mountains, N. Syria and Cyprus).

Publications include *Reise in den cilicischen Taurus über Tarsus*, Gotha, 1858; *Reise nach Cypern und Kleinasien* in *Pettermanns Mitt. X*, 1862.

New taxa described from Turkey by T. Kotschy: *Allium armenum, Crocus karduchorum, Iris junonia*.

Species named in honour of T. Kotschy: *Colchicum kotschyi, Crocus kotschyanus, Gladiolus kotschyanus*.

Biogr. and bibliogr.: Fenzl, E.: Theodor Kotschy in *Alm. Akad. Wien* 17 (1867).

Kurt Krause

Born 1883 in Potsdam; died 19 September 1963 in Berlin. German botanist. Professor at the Botanischer Garten und Botanisches Museum, Berlin. He was Professor of Botany at the Agricultural Institute of Ankara University, between 1933 and 1939. During this time he collected on Ağri Dağ, Erciyas Dağ and around Ankara. Krause's Anatolian collections were kept in the Botanical Museum in Berlin, but they were completely destroyed by air raids on 1 March 1943. There are some duplicates in the Herbarium of the University of Ankara.

Krause's publications include Die floristischen Beziehungen des Ararat-gehietes in *Bot. Jahrb.* 52: 26 (1914); Über die Vegetations verhältnisse des Argaeus (Erciyas Dagh) im Kleinasiens in *Naturwiss.* 241 (1932); Uber die Flora des Gebietes von Kayseri und des Erciyas dagi in Anatolien in *Bot. Jahrb.* 71: 32 (1940); *Zur Flora von Ankara (Ankaranin Floru)*, first published 1934, revised edition 1937; Beiträge zur Flora Kleinasiens in *Fedde, Repert. Spec. Nov.* 22: 293 (1926); loc. cit. 24: 37 (1927); loc. cit. 25: 86 (1928); loc. cit. 26: 322 (1929); loc. cit. 28: 77, 113 (1930); loc. cit. 30: 226 (1932); loc. cit. 33: 321 (1934).

Biogr. and bibliogr.: Çelebioglu, S.: Prof. Dr. Kurt Krause, Der Angesehene Türkophile und Gründer des Türkischen Herbarium zu Ankara in *Turk Biologi Derg.* 8: 61 (1958), and 13: 143 (1963).

Max Leichtlin

Born Karlsruhe, Germany, on 20 October 1831; died in Baden-Baden on 3 September 1910. Leichtlin studied at Karlsruhe Botanic Garden in 1846 and was subsequently employed as a gardener in Frankfurt, Ghent and Potsdam, making botanical expeditions in Europe, Brazil and Argentina. In 1856 he was employed by the famous Ghent nursery of Van Houtte. Seventeen years later, in 1873, he formed a private botanical garden at Baden-Baden and here he specialized in cultivating rare plants and in particular those of a bulbous nature, especially *Iris* and *Lilium*. He introduced many bulbs from Asia and made several visits to various parts of

S.E. Europe and W. Asia in the late nineteenth century. Species named in honour of M. Leichtlin: *Crocus leichtlinii, Lilium leichtlinii, Iris leichtlinii, Iris korolkowii* var. *leichtliniana, Tecophilaea cyanocrocus* var. *leichtlinii*.

Biogr. and bibliogr.: Ascherson, P. F. A. and Graebner, K. O. P.: *Synopsis der Mitteleuropäischen Flora* 3: 178 (1905); *Bot. Mag. Dedic.* 223 (1931).

J. J. Manissadjian

Born 1862; died 1942. Son of a German mother and Armenian father. He studied natural sciences in the University of Berlin and became Professor of Botany at the Anatolian College in Merzifon, Turkey; he was also the creator and curator of the museum at this College. He worked for 25 years in this school, from 1890 onwards, and between 1891 and 1912 he travelled through many regions of Anatolia (Amasya, Merzifon, Kastamonu, Ankara, Trabzon, the Taurus mountains near Adana, the mountains of Antakya, Erek Daği, etc.) and made a rich collection of plants, butterflies and beetles. J. Freyn (1845–1903), the famous Austrian botanist, examined his material and published the results.

The specimens of Manissadjian are distributed in many herbaria, for example Ankara, Berlin, Kew, Paris and Vienna. He sent living material to van Tubergen (Holland) and contributed much to the knowledge of Turkish bulbous plants. After the First World War he moved to America, where he died in 1942.

Species named in honour of J. J. Manissadjian: *Iris manissadjiani, Merendera manissadjiani*.

Biogr. and bibliogr.: van Tubergen: *New bulbous and tuberous rooted plants*, 9, (1947). White, G. E.: Adventuring with Anatolia College, 1940, p. 19, Grinnell, Iowa; Aznavour, G. V.: Etude sur l'Herbier Artistique Tchitouny in *Magyar Bot. Lap.* 16: 5 (1917).

George Maw

Born London 10 December 1832; died Kenley, Surrey, 7 February 1912. Maw studied farming at Cirencester Agricultural College but did not follow this with a farming career. In 1850 he established a tile factory in Shropshire and worked from his home at Benthall Hall at Brosely where he later established a fine collection of bulbs, including Crocus.

He was a great traveller, visiting Asia Minor (mainly W. Turkey), N. Africa and many European countries and in 1871 made a now famous expedition with J. D. Hooker and John Ball to N. Africa.

His knowledge of geology, botany and chemistry was considered to be impressive but he will be largely remembered for his work on *Crocus*. This began in 1875 and, during the next ten years, he visited many of their natural habitats and cultivated over 60 species at Benthall, eventually pouring all his knowledge into a magnificent monograph, *The Genus Crocus*, 1886, which contained 67 coloured plates prepared by himself. Benthall Hall is now a National Trust property with Sir Paul and Lady Benthall, in residence; it was their family home before Maw lived there in the late nineteenth century. There are still many autumn and spring crocuses growing in the garden, undoubtedly dating from the time of Maw's occupancy of the property.

Species named in honour of Maw: *Draba mawii, Saxifraga maweana*.
Species described by Maw: *Crocus boissieri, C. danfordiae, C. hermoneus*.
Biogr. and bibliogr.: *Kew Bull.* 1912: 155 (1912); *Curtis' Bot. Mag. Dedic.*
187 (1931).

Friedrich Wilhelm Noë

Born 1798 in Berlin; died 1 October 1858 in Istanbul. Austrian pharmacist.
In 1844 he settled in Istanbul where he became director of the Botanic
Garden of the Ecole Impériale de Médecine de Galata Serai.
  During his 14 years in Turkey he travelled widely (Uludağ, Tokat, Sivas,
Harput, Diyarbakır, Van, etc.), particularly in 1849–52 and in 1854 when
his son accompanied him; these expeditions resulted in the collection of
many bulbous plants. His specimens are often labelled 'Herbarium
Noeanum', 'Plantes d'Orient' or 'W. Noë – Iter Orientale' and they are to be
located in several herbaria, notably those of Ankara University, Geneva,
Kew, Leiden and Paris.
  The collection in Istanbul was destroyed in 1848 when the Ecole
Impériale de Médecine was burnt down.
  Species named in honour of F. W. Noë: *Allium noeanum*.
  Species described from Turkey by F. W. Noë: *Allium laceratum, A.
zebdanense, Fritillaria kurdica*.
  Biogr. and bibliogr.: Ascherson, P. F. A. and Graebner, K. O. P.:
Synopsis der Mitteleuropäischen Flora 2: 380 (1900); *Österr. Bot. Wochen-
blatt* 3, 36: 368 (1853); Lechler, W. in *Flora* 28: 560 (1845).

Guillaume Antoine Olivier

Born 19 January 1756 at Arcs (Toulon); died 1 October 1814 at Lyon.
French botanist and entomologist who studied medicine in Montpellier and
later travelled with the French physician J. G. Bruguière in Turkey (mainly
S.E. Anatolia), Egypt and Iran in the period 1792–98. His plant specimens
carry on their labels the title of 'Voyage d'Olivier et Bruguière en Orient' and
are to be found mainly in the Paris and Geneva herbaria.
  He published *Voyage dans l'Empire Ottoman, l'Egypte et la Persé*, Paris,
1801–7.
  Species named in honour of G. A. Olivier: *Crocus olivieri, Fritillaria
olivieri*.
  Biogr. and bibliogr.: Silvestre, A. F.: *Notice biographique sur M.
Guillaume Antoine Olivier*, (1815).

Otto Schwarz

Born 1900. German botanist and Professor of Botany at the University of
Jena. He was employed at the Agricultural Institute at Bornova, Izmir,
between 1931 and 1933, during which time he collected in W. Anatolia,
mainly in our Area 6. Schwarz's herbarium collections are deposited mainly
in Ankara, Berlin and Bornova.
  He published several papers on the Turkish flora, for example: Additamentum ad Florulam Lydiae in *Fedde, Rep.* 36: 65 and 129 (1934); Die

Vegetationverhältnisse Westanatoliens in *Bot. Jahrb.* 67: 297 (1935); Phytochorologi als Wissenschaft am Beispiele der Vorderasiatischen Flora in *Fedde, Rep. Beih.* 100: 178 (1938); Anatolica in *Fedde, Rep.* 54: 26 (1944).

New taxa described from Turkey by O. Schwarz: *Allium albo-tunicatum, A. pictistamineum, A. stylosum, A. tmoleum, Crocus elwesii, Iris glockiana, Tulipa hayatii*.

Walter Erdmann Siehe

Born Berlin 1 January 1859; died Adana, Turkey, 10 March 1928. His primary education was in Berlin and later (1878–1880) he attended the Royal Garden School (Königlichen Gärtnerlehranstalt), then the universities of Berlin and Jena.

Siehe is probably one of the most significant personalities in the history of collection and study of Anatolian bulbous plants; he lived in Turkey for more than 25 years and exported to Europe the many native bulbs which he gathered and cultivated in his garden in Fındıkpınar.

Siehe's first excursion to Turkey was in 1895 and two years later he bought 35 acres of land at Fındıkpınar, in Mersin province, with the intention of growing fruit trees and bulbs, assisted by two gardeners, one German and one Russian. From this base he made excursions, both botanical and archaeological, in southern Anatolia, Syria, Mesopotamia and the Caucasus, often collecting dried specimens which are now deposited at various herbaria including Kew and Edinburgh. In 1903 he married Elisabeth Trenkle (after whom *Iris elisabethae* is named) and had two children, Karl Gunther (1906–1971) and Irmgard (now Mrs Dünbier) who was born in 1910 and now lives in Freiburg, Germany. We wish to express out greatest thanks to Mrs Dünbier for some of the information included in this short biography of her father.

During the First World War Siehe worked for a railway company in Turkey (at Belemedik) but he continued collecting and growing plants. However in the latter part of the war the area where he lived was occupied by the French army, and Siehe was imprisoned for 19 months. During this time his house at Fındıkpınar was burnt, the orchards destroyed and the housekeeper and his sons killed; all his property was looted, which included money (reported as 150,000 gold marks), his plant collections, books and pictures (about 4,000). Thus, much valuable information concerning the Turkish bulbous flora was destroyed. After this Siehe could not return to work in Fındıkpınar and in 1924 he resumed working for the railway company, first at Hayfa then in Mersin. In 1928 he died of malaria in the American Hospital at Adana and was buried in Mersin. Although his grave was maintained for a long time, his daughter tells us that she could find no trace of it when she visited in 1971. The graveyard in Mersin where Siehe was buried was removed from there in 1968 and an *Endüstiri Meslek Lisesi* (a vocational school of industry) was built on the area.

On 5 May 1981 T. Baytop visited Fındıkpınar and saw the place where Siehe lived and worked for 25 years, but little has survived. All traces of the bulbs, greenhouses and buildings have disappeared but the spot is marked by a horse chestnut tree which Siehe had planted in front of the house; the site is planted with fruit trees and some small houses have been built. The older members of the village said that Siehe was known as 'the florist'; they remembered that he grew bulbs, kept sheep and horses and had a beautiful collection of guns. The only reminder of Siehe in the area is a type of sour apple introduced by him from Europe and improved in this region where it is today known as the 'florist's apple'.

Siehe published a considerable amount of information about Turkish bulbs, describing many species as new and preparing dried voucher specimens. At one time he catalogued for sale about 100 species native to Anatolia in his 'Oriental Flower Bulbs' list. He planned to publish a book on the Turkish flora but with the destruction of his property this was sadly not to be fulfilled.

Species described by Siehe: *Allium exiguiflorum, A. lycaonicum, Colchicum hydrophilum, C. tauri, Fritillaria syriaca, Iris galatica, I. haussknechtii, I. tauri, Scilla cilicica.*

Species named in honour of Siehe: *Chionodoxa siehei, Colchicum sieheanum, Crocus sieheanus.*

Biogr. and bibliogr.: Ascherson, P. F. A., and Graebner, K. O. P.: *Synopsis der Mitteleuropäischen Flora* 3: 511 (1906); *Mitt. Deutsch Dendrol. Ges.* 1922: 253 (1922); *Gartenwelt* 32: 196 (1928).

Paul Emil Ernst Sintenis

Born 4 June 1847 at Seidenburg (Germany); died 6 March 1907 at Kupferberg (Germany). German plant collector, who gathered a great deal of material in Turkey. Botanical specimens from his collections are widely distributed through the major European herbaria.

His first expedition to Turkey was in 1883 to the Troad (Çanakkale, Truva, Kaz Dağ). Then followed a whole series of expeditions: 1888 to Syria and S.E. Anatolia (Mersin, Iskenderun, nemrut Dağ, Siverek, Diyarbakır, Mardin etc.); 1889 and 1890 to E. Anatolia (Trabzon, Gümüşhane, Harput, Keban, Arapkir, Kemaliye, Erzincan); 1892 to Paphlagonia (Inebolu, Küre, Kastamonu, Tosya); and 1894 to Pontus (Gümüşhane mountains).

New taxa desribed from Turkey by P. Sintenis: *Allium filifolium, Colchicum bifolium, Fritillaria ophioglossifolia, Iris kerneriana, Ornithogalum sigmoideum.*

Species named in honour of P. Sintenis: *Allium sintenisii, Iris sintenisii, Tulipa sintenisii.*

Biogr. and bibliogr.: Cullen, J.: The Turkish collections of Paul Sintenis in *Notes R.B.G. Edin.* 25: 31 (1963).

Pierre de Tchihatcheff

Born 1812 at Gatchina (Leningrad); died 15 October 1890 in Florence. Russian geologist, naturalist and politician. He visited Turkey for the first time in 1842 as attaché in the Russian Embassy at Istanbul and travelled around in Turkey between 1848 and 1863 when he collected a great deal of material; his herbarium specimens are deposited in Geneva, Paris and Leningrad.

Publications by Tchihatcheff include: *Asie Mineure* (8 vols.), Paris,

1852–69, and *Botanique* (2 vols. + atlas), 1860; Etudes sur la végétation des hautes montagnes de l'Asie Mineure et de l'Arménie in *Bull. Soc. Bot. France* 4: 863 (1857).

Species named in honour of P. de Tchihatcheff: *Tchihatchewia isatidea*, *Allium tchihatchewii*.

Joseph Pitton de Tournefort

Born 5 June 1656 at Aix-en-Provence; died 28 December 1707 in Paris. French botanist, explorer and Professor of Botany at the Jardin du Roi in Paris (1683). Tournefort was one of Europe's leading botanists of the period. He travelled widely in Turkey (Gelibolu, Istanbul, Trabzon, Erzurum, Ağrı Dağ, Tokat, Ankara, Bursa, Izmir, etc.) in 1700–02 with the German physician A. Gundelscheimer and the French artist C. Aubriet. The main collection of his specimens is housed in the Paris herbarium but some are also to be found in the British Museum and the Sherard Herbarium, Oxford.

He wrote *Relation d'un voyage du Levant fait par ordre du Roy*, which was published posthumously in 1717, and *Elemens de Botanique*, 1694, a three-volume work which was translated into Latin as *Institutiones rei herbariae*, 1700. His concept of the genus constitutes one of the landmarks in the history of taxonomy.

Species named in honour of J. P. de Tournefort: *Crocus tournefortii*.

Biogr. and bibliogr.: Bonnet, Ed.: Un document inédit, relatif au voyage de Tournefort en Orient in *Bull. du Muséum d'Histoire Naturelle* 16: 247 (1910); *Dictionary of Scientific Biography*, 13: 442 (1976).

Edward Whittall

Born 1851; died 1917. British businessman and collector. He belonged to an English family who settled in 1809 in Izmir and founded there a commercial firm called Whittall and Co. He was an ardent sportsman and organized hunting expeditions into the mountains of Anatolia at least once a year. During these trips he became interested in the local flora, which so fascinated him that eventually horticulture became his principal occupation. His grounds and gardens near Izmir (Bornova) contained trees of great size and variety, and large greenhouses filled with plants.

He opened a flower shop and sent out many of the villagers, during slack business seasons, to scour the mountains for bulbs and other plants. At times, he had as many as 50 men out at once. They were paid liberally, and part of the costs were defrayed by sales of bulbs to the trade in England and Holland. At times there was a considerable surplus of bulbs, and rather than destroy them he created an additional garden at the top of Nif Dağ, a mountain close to Izmir, where a number of men were employed. By 1893 more than a million bulbs had been planted there. Whittall's special study was bulbs, some of which were first introductions to Europe, and some of the new species were named after him.

New taxa described from W. Anatolia by E. Whittall: *Chionodoxa gigantea*, *C. tmoli*, *Crocus mouradii*.

Species named in honour of E. Whittall: *Fritillaria whittallii*, *Tulipa whittallii*.

Biogr. and bibliogr.: Derrick, C. F.: The Whittall family in *Lloyd's Log* 43, 6: 18 (1972); *Quarterly Bull. Alpine Gard. Soc.* 43, 3: 240 (1975).

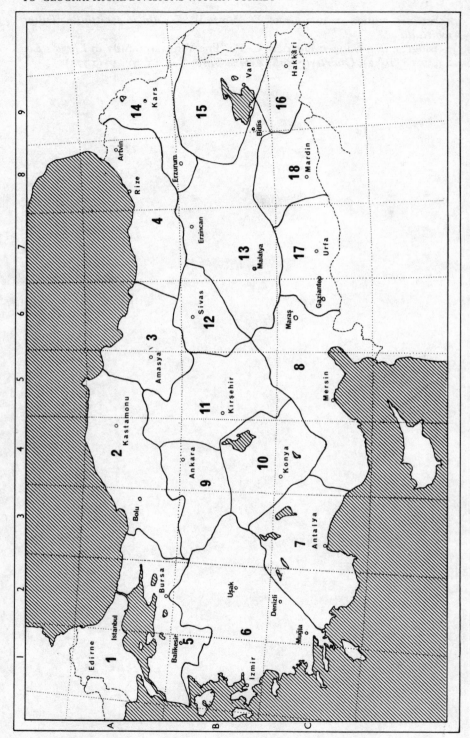

THREE

Geographical Divisions Within Turkey

Attempts to divide Turkey into phytogeographical areas have been made by various authors. There are differences of opinion about the boundaries of these areas. As a basis for our book we have adopted the geographical divisions accepted at the First National Geographical Congress, Ankara, 1941, and numbered the subdivisions. These numbers have been used to indicate the general distribution of the species within Turkey as follows:

Turkey-in-Europe (1)

North Anatolia (2, 3, 4)
   West Black Sea subdivision (2)
   Middle Black Sea subdivision (3)
   East Black Sea subdivision (4)

West Anatolia (5, 6)
   Marmara Sea subdivision (5)
   Aegean Sea subdivision (6)

South Anatolia (7, 8)
   Antalya subdivision (7)
   Adana subdivision (8)

Inner Anatolia (9, 10, 11, 12)
   Upper Sakarya subdivision (9)
   Konya subdivision (10)
   Middle Kızılırmak subdivision (11)
   Upper Kızılırmak subdivision (12)

East Anatolia (13, 14, 15, 16)
   Upper Fırat subdivision (13)
   Erzurum-Kars subdivision (14)
   Upper Murat-Van subdivision (15)
   Hakkâri subdivision (16)

South-East Anatolia (17, 18)
   Middle Fırat subdivision (17)
   Dicle subdivision (18)

FOUR

Classification

As mentioned in the preface, several flowering plant families contain species which have underground storage organs such as bulbs, corms and tubers. In this book we have chosen to deal with only three families of mono-cotyledons: Amaryllidaceae, Iridaceae and Liliaceae, since these constitute the majority of 'bulbous' plants in Turkey. There are of course also species with bulbs (in the wide sense) in other families such as Orchidaceae (*Orchis*, *Ophrys* etc), Araceae (*Arum*, *Biarum*, *Arisarum*), Fumariaceae (*Corydalis*), Primulaceae (*Cyclamen*) and Ranunculaceae (*Anemone*, *Eranthis*).

In the three important families which we are including here we have attempted to mention all the species which have been described from Turkish material or have been recorded from Turkey. Many synonyms are included so that the reader is given at least some information about the name. Names which have been used in an incorrect sense (e.g. *Iris lutescens* sensu Boiss., non Lam.) are also included, but only where the epithet is a well known one, causing confusion when encountered in other literature.

Key to Families

1. Stamens three; leaves usually distichous   **Iridaceae** (p. 28)
1. Stamens six; leaves usually not distichous
    2. Ovary superior   **Liliaceae (including Alliaceae)** (p. 50)
    2. Ovary inferior   **Amaryllidaceae** (p. 21)

FIVE

Amaryllidaceae

A large family of very ornamental bulbous plants, Amaryllidaceae are mainly tropical in distribution but extending into southern Europe and western Asia, especially in the Mediterranean region. The genera in the Old World temperate zone are few and they are not large in number of species. The largest genus, *Narcissus*, has most of its species in Spain and Portugal but a few extend eastwards as far as Turkey. On the other hand, *Galanthus* and *Sternbergia* have their maximum number of species in western Asia, the latter genus having more species in Turkey than any other country. *Ixiolirion* mainly occurs farther to the east but does extend west into eastern Anatolia. *Pancratium* is a coastal plant occurring right round the Mediterranean and is very tropical in appearance. It is the only genus which occurs in the tropics (Africa, India) as well as in Europe and western Asia.

Family description

Bulb scaly, covered with papery tunics. Flowers with six separate or united perianth segments, sometimes with a corona present; stamens six; ovary inferior. Fruit a three-valved capsule.

Key to genera of Amaryllidaceae in Turkey

1. Flowers blue-purple; stem leafy   **2 *Ixiolirion***
1. Flowers white or yellow
2. Flowers without a corona
3. Flowers erect, goblet-shaped   **6 *Sternbergia***
3. Flowers pendulous
4. Inner and outer segments unequal   **1 *Galanthus***
4. Inner and outer segments equal   **3 *Leucojum***
2. Flowers with a corona
5. Corona less than 2 cm deep   **4 *Narcissus***
5. Corona more than 2 cm deep   **5 *Pancratium***

1 *Galanthus* (English: Snowdrop; Turkish: Kardelen, Aktaş)

Small bulbous plants with two basal leaves, rarely three. Flower solitary, nodding; perianth with six segments in two series, the three large outer ones obovate, concave, white; the three inner smaller ones white with a green spot at the apex and sometimes also at the base. Anthers yellow, forming a cone. Capsule three-valved, many-seeded, the seeds globose, blackish or brownish.

A genus of about 20 species in Europe and West Asia. In Turkey seven species, usually occurring in light woodland or scrub.

Snowdrops are much-loved in gardens for their late winter or early spring flowers. They are easily cultivated in cool semi-shaded situations and although all species have an overall similarity there are enough subtle differences to make them of great interest to the specialist. Many cultivars have been selected.

G. byzantinus Baker in Gard. Chron. Ser. 3, 13: 226 (1893)

Leaves slightly greyish green, lanceolate, folded down at the margin, 1–2.5 cm wide. Inner perianth segments with a green spot at the base and apex, or almost wholly green. Woods, or in turf at higher altitudes. March-April. Areas 2, 5 (endemic).

G. plicatus, M. Bieb From Crimea and Roumania. Is very similar but has a green spot only at the apex of the inner segments. Probably occurring in Area 1.

G. cilicicus Baker in Gard. Chron. Ser. 3, 21: 214 (1897)

Leaves grey-green, flat, linear, 5–8 mm wide. Inner perianth segments with a green spot at the apex only. Woods in mountains. December–February. Area 8 (and Syria, Lebanon). This may only be a form of the European G. nivalis L. which is not known to occur in Turkey.

G. elwesii Hooker in Bot. Mag. t. 6166 (1875)

Leaves grey-green, flat, usually 1–3 cm wide, oblanceolate and hooded at apex. Inner perianth segments with a green spot at the base and apex. Woods and rocky shady places. February to April. Areas 6, 7, 8 (and Aegean Is.).

G. fosteri Baker in Gard. Chron. Ser. 3, 5: 458 (1889)

Leaves bright green, not glaucous, flat, 1.5–2.5 cm wide, oblanceolate. Inner perianth segments with a green spot at the base and apex. Rocky places in scrub. February–March. Areas 3, 8 (and Syria, Lebanon).

G. gracilis Čelakô in Sitz.-Ber. Böhm Ges. Wiss. Math.-nat. Cl. 1891: 184 (1891) (Syn. G. graecus)

Leaves grey-green, flat, 5–8 mm wide, linear and twisted lengthways. Inner perianth segments with a green spot at base and apex. Light woodland. March–April. Areas 1, 6, 7 (and Greece and Bulgaria).

G. ikariae Baker in Gard. Chron. ser. 3, 13: 506 (1893) (Syn. G. latifolius Rupr.)

Leaves bright green, not glaucous, flat, 1–2 cm wide, strap-shaped and recurved. Inner perianth segments with a green spot at apex. Rocky shady places. March–April. Area 4 (and Caucasus). Subsp. ikariae is very similar, differing in having much broader outer perianth segments. It is confined to a few islands in the Aegean Sea.

G. nivalis L. subsp. reginae-olgae (Orph.) Gottl.-Tann. in *Abh. Zool-bot. Ges. Wien* 2, 4: 32 (1904)

Leaves grey-green, flat, linear, 3–5 mm wide, appearing after the flowers, in late autumn. Inner perianth segments with a green spot at the apex only. Light woodland. October–November. Areas ?6, 7 (and in Greece).

G. rizehensis F. Stern, *Snowdrops and Snowflakes*: 37 (1956)

Leaves dull dark green, sometimes very slightly glaucous, flat, 4–6 mm wide, linear, recurved. Inner perianth segments with a green spot at the apex. Sparse woods. February–March. Area 4 (endemic).

Other species recorded in literature for Turkey are *G. transcaucasicus* Fomin and *G. caucasicus* (Baker) Grossh., but these records have not been confirmed.

On 12 May 1979, we were travelling in the Taurus mountains in the vicinity of Gündoğmus and, during a rain storm, were given hospitality by a family living in a stone mountain hut during the summer grazing period. It was a surprise to find that they were not only shepherds but also bulb collectors. They, and other families in the area, gather bulbs and plants of *Galanthus elwesii*, *Eranthis cilicica*, *Eremurus*, etc., using short-handled pick-axes made specifically for the purpose in the nearby village. The bulbs are partly dried and then await collection by a 'middle-man' who visits a number of villages in order to accumulate a large quantity.

The bulbs are then taken to an export firm in Antalya (there are also similar firms in Izmir and Istanbul) where they are cleaned, graded into sizes and exported. At this stage any small bulbs are separated and planted into nursery beds until they are large enough to sell. In 1979 the collectors were paid 25 Turkish Lira (equivalent of about 30 English pence) per kilogram, in the case of *Galanthus elwesii*.

We purchased from them 7 kilos of recently dug bulbs for cultivation in Istanbul and England, where they flowered in the winter of 1980. The family we encountered said that they had been collecting bulbs for about 20 years.

2 *Ixiolirion*

A small genus with only one species, widely distributed in south-west and central Asia.

This interesting plant, with its showy blue trumpet-shaped flowers, is not well-known in gardens although it is often obtainable from nurserymen. It requires a hot sunny situation and the bulbs should be planted deeply, at least 10 cm.

I. tataricum (Pallas) Herbert, *App.*: 37 (1821) (*I. montanum* (Labill.) Herbert)

Bulbous plant with narrowly linear stem leaves. Flowers several, in umbels or short racemes, blue-violet, funnel-shaped. Stamens six, inserted at the base of the perianth segments; stigma three-lobed. Capsule coriaceous, oblong-clavate, three-valved, dehiscent in the upper part, containing many ovoid-oblong seeds. April–June. Fields, roadsides and grassy places. Areas 8, 13, 14, 15, 16, 17, 18 (and widespread in west and central Asia).

3 *Leucojum* (English: Snowflake; Turkish: Akçabardak)

A genus of nine species, distributed in S. Europe and N. Africa as far east as the Caucasus. Most of them occur in the western Mediterranean. In Turkey there is one species: *L. aestivum* L.

L. aestivum L., *Syst. Nat.* ed. 10: 975 (1759)

Robust bulbous plant up to 50 cm tall with a compressed stem. Leaves basal, 2–5, strap-like, deep green. Flowers nodding, two to seven in an umbel, broadly bell-shaped, up to 3.5 cm diameter, white with a green tip to each of the six free perianth segments. Fruit a globose capsule containing many black seeds. Wet meadows and marshy places near rivers and ponds. March–May. Areas 1, 2, 5 (and widespread in Europe). A very ornamental plant, widely grown in gardens. It has been used medicinally, the fresh bulb being an emetic, externally resolvent. It is a graceful plant for growing in damp situations in full sun or slightly shaded areas. It is particularly effective when placed at the edge of a pond where its slender stems and dangling white flowers can be seen reflected in the water.

4 *Narcissus* (English: Daffodil; Turkish: Nergis)

Bulbous plants with strap-like narrowly linear or filiform basal leaves. Inflorescence a scape bearing a solitary flower or several in an umbel. Perianth with six segments joined into a tube and a cup-shaped or bell-shaped corona. Stamens six, inserted in the perianth tube. Fruit a three-valved capsule containing many black seeds.

A well known genus widespread in Europe, N. Africa and W. Asia but mainly centred in western Europe and containing about 60 species. In Turkey there are only two truly wild species.

In the time of the Ottoman Empire many horticultural forms were cultivated in Istanbul. These forms were given Turkish names which described the shape of the corona, and for each form there were often several 'sub-forms', e.g. 'Sadekehruba'. Ubeydi mentions 269 cultivated forms and gives descriptions.[133]

In Roman times in southern Anatolia (Izmir, Antalya) some Narcissi were cultivated for the extraction of essential oils. It is still possible to find some of these naturalized in these areas, including double forms. Near Istanbul in the Belgrat forest, *N. pseudonarcissus* L. in a double form is naturalized; near Van *N. poeticus* L. (*Zerrinkadeh* = 'Golden Cup') is cultivated in gardens and may be found as an escape in nearby wild situations and near Izmir *N. papyraceus* is naturalized. There are notes on the history of *Narcissus* in Turkey by S. Ünver.[135]

In Turkey only one species, *N. tazetta*, is of horticultural importance. This is not often cultivated in its wild form but has given rise to a number of selections and hybrids. This strongly fragrant, early-flowering cluster-headed narcissus is very popular as a cut flower in single and double forms.

N. serotinus L. *Sp. Pl.*: 290 (1753)
Autumn-flowering, often with no leaves present. Leaves filiform. Scape about 25 cm tall carrying one or two scented white flowers 2–2.5 cm diameter, with a shallow yellow cup. In maquis at low altitudes. October–November. Areas ?1, 5, 6, 7, 8 (and widespread in Mediterranean region).

N. tazetta L., *Sp. Pl.*: 290 (1753)
Winter- or spring-flowering, with leaves present. Leaves strap-like. Scape up to 50 cm tall, carrying up to 20 flowers in an umbel. Flowers sweetly scented, 2–5 cm diameter, usually with white perianth segments and a shallow yellow cup. Fields and waste places near cultivation. November–March. Areas 1, 5, 6, 7, 8, 18 (and widespread in Mediterranean region).

There are many variants of this species, often given specific status, such as the large-flowered *N. cypri* Haw. which may be found in Turkey. The 'species' known as *N. orientalis*, *N. byzantinus* and *N.constantinopolitanus* were all ancient forms of *N. tazetta* sent to Europe from Istanbul (Constantinople).

5 *Pancratium* (English: Sea Lily; Turkish: Kumzambağı)

A small genus but widespread in the Mediterranean, Africa and India, mainly tropical but two or three species occur in temperate regions. In Turkey there is one species: *P. maritimum*. Although a rather striking plant with its large white daffodil-like fragrant flowers, *P. maritimum* is seldom cultivated. It is not very hardy and will only survive in mild districts without protection and even then is usually rather reluctant to produce its fleeting flowers.

P. maritimum L., *Sp. Pl.*: 291 (1753)
Bulb very large, producing a tuft of basal strap-like grey-green leaves. Scape up to 30 cm tall, with an umbel of three to six fragrant large white flowers. The six perianth segments are narrow and rather flimsy and the toothed cup is much larger than that of a Narcissus. Fruit a three-valved capsule containing many flat seeds. August–September. Sandy sea shores. Areas 5, 6, 7, 8 (and widespread in Mediterranean region).

6 *Sternbergia*

Bulbous plants with basal linear or strap-like, synanthous or hysteranthous leaves. Flowers solitary, yellow, or white in one species, erect and infundibuliform, produced in autumn or spring, either on a scape or nearly stemless at ground level. Perianth segments six, fused at the base into a short to rather long tube. Stamens six, of unequal lengths. Style long, simple, with a capitate stigma. Fruit a capsule containing many large black or brown seeds.

As garden plants one species, *S. lutea*, is popular for its autumnal yellow crocus-shaped flowers. The other species are also worthy of cultivation and are yellow-flowered except for the newly discovered white, fragrant, *S. candida* which flowers in spring. They require warm sunny situations where the bulbs will ripen well in summer.

S. candida Mathew & T. Baytop in *The Garden* 104: 302 (1979)

Leaves grey-green, strap-like, about 1 cm wide. Flowers white, 4–5 cm long, fragrant, produced on stems up to 25 cm long together with the leaves in spring. January–February. Edge of Cedar forests. Area 7 (endemic).

S. clusiana (Ker-Gawler) Ker-Gawler ex Sprengel, *Syst. Veg.* 2: 57 (1825)

Leaves grey-green, strap-like, about 1–2 cm wide. Flowers large, yellow, up to 7 cm long, produced before the leaves in autumn, nearly stemless at ground level. September–October. Fields and dryish hills. Areas 6, 7, 8, 13, 17, 18 (and Syria, Lebanon, Israel, Iraq, Iran).

S. colchiciflora Waldst. & Kit., *Pl. Rar. Hung.* 2: 172, t. 159 (1803–4)

Leaves deep green or grey-green, narrowly linear, 1–2 mm wide. Flowers small, yellow, up to 3 cm long, produced before the leaves in autumn, stemless at ground level. August–September. Edges of fields, dry steppe and rocky places. Areas 1, 3, 5, 6, 7, 8, 10, 17, 18 (widespread, from Yugoslavia east to Crimea, Caucasus and Iran).

S. fischeriana (Herbert) Rupr. in *Gartenfl.* 17: 100, t. 576 (1868)

Leaves grey-green or glossy green, strap-like, about 1 cm diameter. Flowers yellow, 3–4 cm long, produced on stems up to 20 cm long together with the leaves in spring. January–March. Areas 6, 7, 8 (and Caucasus, Iran, Iraq and Syria).

S. lutea (L.) Ker-Gawler ex Sprengel, *Syst. Veg.* 2: 57 (1825)

Leaves dark or glossy green, strap-like, about 5–15 mm wide. Flowers yellow, 4–5 cm long, produced on stems up to 20 cm long, together with the leaves in autumn. September–October. Areas 3, 5, 6, 7 (and widespread in Mediterranean regions).

S. sicula Tineo ex Guss., *Fl. Sic. Syn.* 2: 811 (1845)

(Syn. *S. lutea* var. *graeca* Reichb., *S. lutea* subsp. *sicula* (Tineo ex Guss.) D. Webb). Leaves dark green, linear, about 2–4 mm wide. Flowers yellow, 2.5–4 cm long, produced on short stems up to 5 cm long together with or slightly before the leaves in autumn. September–October. Area 6 (and southern Italy and Greece).

S. schubertii Schenk Described from Torbali in western Turkey in 1840, is probably a form of this with an unusually long perianth tube (1.5–1.8 cm); *S. sicula* has a tube 1 cm or less long. No plant exactly like that described as *S. schubertii* has been recollected in the area.

SIX

Iridaceae

A large family of ornamental rhizomatous, cormous or rarely bulbous plants, widespread throughout most regions of the world but mainly from temperate zones. The family is well represented in western Asia, the main genera being *Iris* and *Crocus*.

Family description

Stock a rhizome, tunicated corm or bulb. Flowers with six equal or unequal segments, often the inner three differing in size and shape from the outer three. Stamens three, opposite the exterior segments. Ovary inferior. Style with three to many branches, these petaloid or slender and filiform.

Key to the genera of Iridaceae in Turkey

1. Flowers zygomorphic   **2 *Gladiolus***

   Flowers actinomorphic   **2**

2. Style branches slender, non-petaloid   **3**

   Style branches expanded and petaloid   **4**

3. Perianth tube 1 cm or less long   **6 *Romulea***

   Perianth tube at least 2 cm   **1 *Crocus***

4. Plants with a subglobose corm; leaves channelled   **3 *Gynandriris***

   Plants with rhizomes or bulbs or tubers; if leaves channelled, bulb not
      with netted tunics   **5**

5. Stock a creeping tuber producing square-section leaves and greenish
      flowers; ovary 1-locular   **4 *Hermodactylus***

   Stock bulbous or rhizomatous; ovary 3-locular   **5 *Iris***

1 *Crocus* (English: Crocus, Saffron; Turkish: Çiğdem)

The name Saffron is of oriental origin, from the Arabic *Za'ferân*.

   Low, stemless plants with tunicated corms, the tunics membranous or fibrous. Leaves produced with or after the flowers, narrowly linear with a whitish or silvery median stripe, the underside with two grooves on either side of a flattish keel. Flowers autumnal or vernal, erect, wine-glass shaped, with six perianth segments joined into a long tube. Stamens three, inserted at the throat. Ovary subterranean until just before maturity when it is carried to the surface on the rapidly elongating pedicel. Style filiform, splitting into three or more yellow to orange-red branches. Fruit a three-valved, many-seeded capsule. Seeds about 2–4 mm long, globose or ellipsoid.

A genus of about 80 species occurring only in Europe and Asia from Portugal east to the Tien Shan and Ala Tau mountains in Russia. In Turkey there are about 30 species.

Nearly all *Crocus* species are of ornamental value and are very popular garden plants. The style branches of *C. sativus* are dried and are well-known as the dye, flavouring agent and medicine called Saffron or Safran; it has a very high vitamin B_2 content. *C. sativus* has been grown in Anatolia for a very long time. In the Hittite period it was cultivated and appears on a tablet found at Boğazköy (Hattusa). The Hittite name for Saffron is Azupiru[50]. At the present time at Safranbolu (= 'plenty of Saffron') it is still grown in fields and is used for the purposes mentioned above, under the name Zerde.

The corms of some *Crocus* (eg. *C. cancellatus* and *C. kotschyanus*) are collected in spring and eaten either raw or baked in hot ashes. Small bundles of *C. cancellatus* corms are sold for this purpose in the bazaars of some eastern Anatolian towns (Gaziantep, Diyarbakır, Urfa, etc.). In some areas, for example, Refahiye, a special meal, called *çiğdem pilavı* (Crocus pilav) is prepared by cooking the corms with *bulgur* (cracked wheat) or rice. In northern Anatolia (Bafra) the corms are used in the preparation of a kind of omelette.

Most of the numerous Turkish species of Crocus are attractive enough to be of garden value and some are already popular, such as *C. speciosus*, *C. biflorus*, *C. chrysanthus* and *C. flavus*. There are spring and autumn-flowering species in a wide range of colours and they are mostly of easy cultivation in well-drained situations.

We have arranged the Turkish species in two groups, *Spring-flowering* and *Autumn-flowering*; within these groups the species are alphabetical.

Spring-flowering

C. abantensis T. Baytop & B. Mathew in *Kew Bull*. 30, 2: 243 (1975)

Corm tunic of netted fibres. Flowers blue or lilac-blue; throat yellow; anthers yellow; style three-branched, orange. April. In short turf. Area 5 (endemic). Resembles *C. biflorus* in flower, but the corms are quite different.

C. adanensis T. Baytop & B. Mathew in *Kew Bull*. 30, 2: 245 (1975)

Corm tunic papery with parallel fibres. Flowers lilac-blue; throat white; anthers yellow; style three-branched. March. Edge of woods and in scrub. Area 8 (endemic).

C. aerius Herbert in *Jour. Hort. Soc. London* 2: 288 (1847) (Syn. *C. biliottii* Maw)

Corm tunic papery with parallel fibres. Flowers pale blue, strongly veined darker violet; throat pale yellow or whitish; anthers yellow; style three-branched, orange. April–May. Grassy mountain slopes. Area 4 (endemic).

C. ancyrensis (Herbert) Maw in *Gard. Chron.* 1881: 528 (1881)
Corm tunic of netted fibres. Flowers wholly yellow-orange, sometimes with a purple tube; throat yellow; anthers yellow; style three-branched, orange to reddish. February–April. Open rocky places or in light woodland. Areas 2, 3, 8, 9, 10, 11 (endemic).

C. antalyensis B. Mathew in *Kew Bull.* 27, 2: 327 (1972)
Corm tunic papery with parallel fibres. Flowers blue or violet, often with greyish speckling on the exterior; throat yellow; anthers yellow; style six-branched. February–March. Sparse woodland or scrub. Areas 5, 6, 7 (endemic).

C. baytopiorum B. Mathew in *Kew Bull.* 29: 88 (1974)
Corm tunic of netted fibres. Flowers clear pale blue with fine veining; throat white or very pale yellow; anthers yellow; style three-branched, yellow or orange. February–April. Limestone screes. Area 7 (endemic).

C. biflorus Miller, *Gard. Dict.* ed. 8, no. 4 (1768)
Corm tunic membranous or shell-like with rings at base. Flowers white to lilac-blue, often striped or veined darker on the outside; throat yellow; anthers yellow, greyish or blackish; style three-branched, yellow to orange-red. February–May. Turkish name: *Kamiş çiğdemi*.

In Turkey there are 10 subspecies:

Subsp. *biflorus*. Leaves three to five, equal to or longer than flowers. Flowers white or lilac with conspicuous brown or purple stripes on the exterior of each outer segment; anthers yellow. Dryish grassy places. Area 5 (and in Italy, Sicily, Rhodes).

Subsp. *adamii* (Gay) B. Mathew. Leaves three to four, shorter than the flowers. Flowers lilac with three to five purple stripes on the exterior of each outer segment; anthers yellow. Dryish grassy places. Area 1 (and in S. Yugoslavia, Bulgaria, Crimea, Caucasus, northern Iran).

Subsp. *artvinensis* (Philippov) B. Mathew. Leaves five to eight, equal to or longer than the flowers. Flowers lilac-violet with one dark stripe on the exterior of each outer segment; anthers yellow. Rocky places. Area 4 (endemic).

Subsp. *crewei* (Hook. fil.) B. Mathew (Syn. *C. crewei* Hook. fil.). Leaves two to three, equal or to just overtopping the flowers. Flowers white (? or lilac) with conspicuous violet stripes on the exterior of each outer segment; anthers blackish-maroon. Rocky slopes and pinewoods. Areas 6, 7 (? and in Cyclades).

Subsp. *isauricus* (Siehe ex Bowles) B. Mathew. Leaves four to seven, shorter than or just reaching the flowers. Flowers white or lilac, striped or speckled purple on the exterior of the outer segments; anthers yellow but usually with a greyish median line (connective). Rocky hillsides. Areas 6, 7, 8, 10 (endemic).

Subsp. *nubigena* (Herbert) B. Mathew. Leaves four to eight, equal to or overtopping the flowers. Flowers white or lilac with conspicuous purple stripes on the exterior of the outer segments; anthers blackish-maroon; style branches finely pubescent. Rocky places. Areas 5, 6, 7 (and in Aegean Is.).

Subsp. *pseudonubigena* B. Mathew. Leaves five to eight, shorter than or sometimes equalling the flowers. Flowers white or lilac, conspicuously striped on the exterior of the outer segments; anthers blackish-maroon; style branches glabrous. In dryish scrub. Areas 8, 13, 17, 18 (endemic).

Subsp. *pulchricolor* (Herbert) B. Mathew. Leaves three to five, shorter than the flowers. Flowers usually rich blue-violet, usually stained darker at the base but not conspicuously striped; anthers yellow. Moist alpine turf or pinewoods, near melting snow. Areas 2, 5 (endemic).

Subsp. *punctatus* B. Mathew. Leaves four to five, equalling the flowers. Flowers pale to mid-lilac, unstriped, but minutely speckled violet on the exterior of the outer segments; anthers yellow usually with black basal lobes. Dry grassy or stony places, often in scrub. Area 7 (endemic).

Subsp. *tauri* (Maw) B. Mathew (Syn. *C. tauri* Maw). Leaves four to nine, shorter than or equalling the flowers. Flowers pale to mid-lilac, not prominently striped but sometimes finely darker-veined; anthers yellow. Rocky slopes and in scrub, often near melting snow. Areas 4, 8, 11, 12, 13, 14, 15 (and in N. Iraq, N.W. Iran).

C. boissieri Maw in *Gard. Chron.* 1881, 2: 304 (1881)

Probably spring-flowering. Corm tunic unknown. Leaves three, rather broad. Flowers wholly white or pale lilac; throat white; anthers yellow; style yellow or orange, shortly and rather obscurely lobed at the apex. Originally collected in June. Habitat unknown. ?Area 8.

C. boissieri is known only as an incomplete dried specimen in the Boissier Herbarium, Geneva. It was said to have been collected by Tchihatcheff on 30 June 1853 at the cave of Corycus (now near a place called Cennet) in Içel province, near Silifke. The specimen is good but has no corm so that it is impossible to ascertain the relationship to other species. One can see that it has long filaments and short anthers, making it distinct from all other Turkish Crocus. We have made several excursions to the type locality but without success. It is extremely unlikely that any Crocus would be flowering on 30 June in this locality, which is only 100 metres above sea level. Probably the information given on the label is incorrect.

C. candidus Clarke, *Travels* 2: 145 (1812)

Corm tunic papery with parallel fibres at base. Flowers white, usually speckled or suffused on the outside with grey-blue; throat yellow; anthers yellow; style six-branched, yellow or orange. February–March. In maquis at low altitudes. Area 5 (endemic). This often has only one or two broad leaves.

C. chrysanthus (Herbert) Herbert in *Bot. Reg.* 29, misc. 83 (1843)

Corm tunic papery with rings at base. Flowers wholly yellow, or with brownish striping or speckling on the outside; throat yellow; anthers yellow or occasionally blackish; style three-branched, yellow to orange. February–April. Open hillsides in turf or in sparse woods or scrub. Areas 1, 5, 6, 7, 8, 9, 10, 11, 12, 13 (and in Balkans).

C. danfordiae Maw in *Gard. Chron.* 1881: 781 (1881)

Corm tunic papery with rings at base. Flowers very small with segments less than 2 cm long, pale lilac-blue, pale yellow or white, often with speckling on the exterior; throat pale yellow or white; anthers yellow; style three-branched, yellow or orange. February–March. Open hillsides or in scrub or pine woods. Areas 8, 9, 10, 11, 12 (endemic).

C. flavus Weston, *Univ. Bot.* 2: 237 (1771) subsp. *flavus*

Corm tunic papery with parallel fibres at base. Flowers yellow throughout; throat yellow; anthers yellow; style three-lobed at the apex. March–April. Woods, scrub and grassland. Area 1, 5 (and in Balkans).

Subsp. *dissectus* T. Baytop and B. Mathew (Syn. *C. mouradii* Whittall) is similar to subsp. *flavus* but with the style divided into six or more branches. Areas 5, 6, 7 (? also in N. Greece).

C. fleischeri Gay in *Bull. Sci. Nat. Geol.* 25: 319 (1832) (Syn. *C. smyrnensis* Poech)

Corm tunic fibrous, the fibres interwoven. Flowers white, often stained purple or brownish-purple on the tube and base of segments; throat yellow; anthers yellow; style six- to many-branched, orange or scarlet. January–April. Rocky hillsides and sparse scrub. Areas 6, 7, 8 (and in Chios).

C. gargaricus Herbert in *Bot. Mag.* sub t. 3866 (1841) subsp. *gargaricus*

Corm tunic netted-fibrous. Flowers wholly yellow or orange-yellow; throat yellow; anthers yellow; style three-branched, orange. April–June. Alpine turf near snow. Areas 5, 6 (endemic). Known only from Kaz Dağ and Göktepe.

Subsp. *herbertii* B. Mathew is similar but has finely netted corm tunics and the corms produce stolons freely. April–June. Damp alpine meadows. Area 5 (endemic). Known only from Ulu Dağ.

C. graveolens Boiss. & Reuter ex Boiss., *Fl. Or.* 5: 107 (1882)

Corm tunic papery, splitting into parallel fibres. Flowers yellow, sometimes marked with bronze striping or suffusion on the outside; throat yellow; anthers yellow; style divided into many slender branches, orange or yellow. February–April. Stony hills and in scrub or light woodland. Areas 8, 10, 17 (and Syria, ?Lebanon). Very similar to *C. vitellinus* but with five to ten, narrower, grey-green leaves.

C. leichtlinii (Dewar) Bowles, *Handbook of Crocus and Colchicum*: 142 (1924)

Corm tunic shell-like with triangular teeth. Flowers blue; throat yellow, anthers greyish or greenish; style three-branched, yellow. March–April. Open rocky slopes. Areas 13, 17 (endemic).

C. olivieri Gay in *Bull. Sci. Nat. Geol.* 25: 319 (1831). subsp. *olivieri*

Corm tunic papery, splitting into parallel fibres at base. Flowers wholly yellow to orange-yellow; throat yellow; anthers yellow; style divided into six yellow to orange branches. February–April. Open rocky or grassy places or light woodland. Areas 1, 2, 5, 6, 9, 10, 11 (and in Balkans).

Subsp. *balansae* Gay ex Baker differs in having 12 to 15 style branches and the flowers are marked on the outside with brown or purplish stripes or staining. January–March. Open hills and maquis. Area 6 (endemic).

Subsp. *istanbulensis* B. Mathew is similar to subsp. *olivieri* but has a wholly parallel-fibrous corm tunic, slightly netted at the apex. March. Dryish scrub. Area 5 (endemic).

C. pestalozzae Boiss., *Diagn. Pl. Or. Nov.* Ser. 1, 13: 17 (1853)

Corm tunic papery with rings at base. Flowers small, clear blue or white with a small black spot at the base of each filament; throat yellow; anthers yellow; style three-branched, orange. January–March. In short turf and stony hills. Areas 1, 5 (endemic).

C. reticulatus Steven ex Adams in Weber fil. & Mohr, *Beitr. Naturk.* 1: 45 (1805) subsp. *reticulatus*

Corm tunic netted-fibrous. Flowers white or lilac-blue, strongly striped with purple or violet on the outside; throat yellow; anthers yellow; style three-branched, yellow to orange. February–May. Rocky places and in scrub. Areas 3, 8 (and in Balkans).

Subsp. *hittiticus* T. Baytop & B. Mathew is very similar but has black anthers. Rocky places. Area 8 (endemic).

C. sieheanus Barr ex B. L. Burtt in *Bot. Mag.* t. 9583 (1939)

Corm tunic papery, splitting into parallel or weakly netted fibres. Flowers wholly yellow or orange-yellow; throat yellow; anthers yellow; style three-branched, orange. April–May. Open hillsides and sparse woods. Areas 8, 10, 11 (endemic).

C. vitellinus Wahlenb. in J. Berggren, *Resor* 2: 59 (1826)

Corm tunic papery, splitting into parallel fibres. Flowers yellow, sometimes with brownish stripes or suffusion on the outside; throat yellow; anthers yellow; style divided into many slender branches, orange or yellow. March–April. Grassy places or light woodland in mountains. Area 8 (and in Syria and Lebanon). Very similar to *C. graveolens* but with two to four, broader green leaves.

Autumn-flowering

C. asumaniae B. Mathew & T. Baytop in *Notes Roy. Bot., Gard. Edinb.* 37, 3: 469 (1979)

Corm tunic finely netted-fibrous. Leafless at flowering time. Flowers white or very faintly lilac; throat white or pale yellow; anthers yellow; style three-branched, the branches orange-red and 1.3–2 cm long. October–November. In sparse oak woodland. Area 7 (endemic).

C. cancellatus Herbert in *Bot. Mag.* sub t. 3864 (1841)

Corm tunic coarsely netted-fibrous. Leafless at flowering time or leaf tips just visible. Flowers white or lilac-blue, usually veined darker and sometimes stained violet-blue at the base of the segments; throat usually pale to deep yellow, sometimes whitish; anthers yellow or rarely white; style divided into several to many slender yellow to reddish-orange branches. September–November. Open rocky places and in sparse woods and scrub. Turkish name: *Yünlü çiğdem*.

In Turkey five subspecies are recognized:

Subsp. *cancellatus* (Syn. *C. cancellatus* var. *cilicicus* Maw, *C. cilicicus* Maw). Flowers pale to mid lilac-blue; throat pale yellow. Perianth segments oblanceolate, acute or subacute, 0.7–1.1 cm wide at widest point. Style divided into many orange branches, usually overtopping the anthers. The corm tunic is more finely netted than in all the other subspecies. Area 8 (and N. W. Syria, Lebanon, Israel).

Subsp. *damascenus* (Herbert) B. Mathew (Syn. *C. damascenus* Herbert, *C. edulis* Boiss. & Blanche). Flowers very pale lilac to mid lilac; throat white or very pale yellow. Perianth segments usually narrowly oblanceolate, 0.4–1 cm wide. Style divided into rather few pale yellow to orange branches. The corm tunic is extremely coarsely netted, more so than in any other subspecies. Areas 8, 10, 12, 13, 15, 16, 17, 18 (and in Syria, N. Iraq, Lebanon, Israel, Jordan, Iran).

Subsp. *mazziaricus* (Herbert) B. Mathew. Flowers white to deep lilac-blue; throat pale yellow. Perianth segments usually obovate, obtuse or subacute, 1–1.8 cm wide. Style divided into many yellow to orange branches, usually overtopping the anthers. Areas 6, ?7 (and in Greece and S. Yugoslavia).

Subsp. *lycius* B. Mathew. Flowers white; throat deep yellow. Style divided into many deep orange or reddish branches, equalling or shorter than the anthers. Area 7 (endemic).

Subsp. *pamphylicus* B. Mathew differs from all other subspecies by having white anthers. Flowers white or pale lilac; throat deep yellow or orange. Style divided into several to many deep orange branches, equalling or shorter than the anthers. Areas 7, 8 (endemic).

C. karduchorum Kotschy ex Maw in *Gard. Chron.* 16: 234 (1881)

Corm tunic thinly membranous, the corm lying on its side in the soil. Leafless at flowering time. Flowers lilac-blue; throat white; anthers white; style dividing into about 20 or more branches, white. September–October. In oak scrub. Area 15 (endemic).

C. kotschyanus K. Koch in *Ind. Sem. Hort. Berol.* 1853: 17 (1853)

Corm tunic thinly membranous. Leafless at flowering time. Flowers lilac-blue or white; throat white with a ring of yellow blotches at the base of the segments; anthers white; style dividing into three to several branches, yellow.

In Turkey four subspecies are recognized:

Subsp. *kotschyanus*. Corm somewhat flattened or misshapen, but upright. Flowers lilac-blue with conspicuous yellow blotches in the throat; throat pubescent. September–October. Mountain meadows and open stony places. Areas 8, 11, 12, 13 (and in north-west Syria, Lebanon).

Subsp. *cappadocicus* B. Mathew. Corm lying on its side in the soil.

Flowers lilac-blue with conspicuous yellow blotches in the throat; throat glabrous. September. Open rocky slopes and alpine turf. Areas 11, 12, 13 (endemic).

Subsp. *hakkariensis* B. Mathew. Corm lying on its side in the soil. Flowers lilac-blue with faint yellow blotches in the throat; throat pubescent. September–October. Rocky or gravelly places in the mountains. Area 16 (endemic).

Subsp. *suworowianus* (K. Koch) B. Mathew (Syn. *C. vallicola* var. *suworowianus* (K. Koch) Maw). Corm lying on its side. Flowers creamy white, sometimes veined violet, with pale yellow blotches in the throat; throat glabrous. August–October. Dryish turf and bare rocky places. Areas 4, 13, 14 (and S. Caucasus).

This is superficially similar to *C. vallicola* but does not have the long-pointed perianth segments, so characteristic of that species; the throat of *C. vallicola* is pubescent.

C. karsianus Fomin is a small-flowered variant of subsp. *suworowianus* and should be regarded as a synonym.

C. pallasii Goldb. in *Mém. Soc. Nat. Moscou* 5: 157 (1817)

Corm tunic finely netted-fibrous. Leafless at flowering time or leaves clearly visible. Flowers pale to deep lilac-blue, or reddish-purple, often veined darker; throat white or lilac; anthers yellow; style three-branched, red or reddish-orange, rarely yellow. September–November. Rocky places or in sparse woods or scrub.

In Turkey there are three subspecies:

Subsp. *pallasii* (Syn. *C. olbanus* Siehe; *C. elwesii* (Maw) O. Schwarz). Corm with a short neck at apex, less than 2 cm long; perianth segments lilac-blue, elliptic, obovate or oblanceolate, often blunt to rounded. Style branches red. Areas 1, 5, 6, 7, 8 (and in Crimea, Balkans, ?Syria, Lebanon, ?Israel).

Subsp. *turcicus* B. Mathew. Corm with a long neck usually 3.5–6 cm long; perianth segments lilac-blue, oblanceolate, often acuminate or acute. Style branches red. Areas 13, 17, 18 (and in N.E. Iran, Lebanon).

Subsp. *dispathaceus* (Bowles) B. Mathew differs from both other subspecies in having reddish-purple perianth segments only 4–7 mm wide and yellow or pale orange style branches. Areas 8, 10 (and in N. Syria).

C. pulchellus Herbert in *Bot. Mag.* sub t. 3862 (1841)

Corm tunic shell-like with rings at base. Leafless at flowering time. Flowers lilac-blue with darker veining; throat deep yellow; anthers white; style many-branched, orange. September–October. Grassy places and in scrub. Areas 1, 5 (and in Balkans).

C. sativus L., *Sp. Pl.*: 36 (1753)

A cultivated plant, sometimes found as a relic of cultivation. Corm tunic finely netted-fibrous. Leaves usually clearly visible at flowering time. Flowers very large, deep lilac-purple with darker veins and a dark stain at the base of the segments; throat white or lilac; anthers yellow; style three-branched, red, the branches 2.5–3.2 cm long. October–December. Still cultivated at Safranbolu. Area 2. Saffron (Turkish: *Safran*) is the dried style branches of this species.

C. scharojanii Rupr. in *Gartenfl.* 17: 134 (1968) (Syn. *C. lazicus* Boiss. & Bal. ex Boiss.)

Corm tunic thinly membranous-fibrous. Leafless at flowering time. Flowers wholly orange-yellow; throat yellow; anthers creamy-yellow; style dividing into three short branches, orange. July–September. Damp alpine turf. Area 4 (and in Caucasus).

C. speciosus M. Bieb., *Beschr. Länd. Terek Casp.*: 129 (1800) subsp. *speciosus*

Corm tunic shell-like with rings at base. Leafless at flowering time. Flowers large, pale lilac-blue to deep purple-blue with prominent darker veining; throat white; anthers yellow; style overtopping the anthers, usually many-branched, yellow or orange. September–November. Woods and meadows. Areas 2, 4, 10, 11, 12 (and in Greece, Crimea, Caucasus and Iran).

Subsp. *ilgazensis* B. Mathew is similar but smaller-flowered with only six to eight style branches which are overtopped by the anthers; the corm tunic is thinly papery, splitting into parallel fibres. September–October. Alpine meadows and clearings in conifer woods. Areas 2, 3, ?4 (endemic).

Subsp. *xantholaimos* B. Mathew differs from both of the other subspecies by having a yellow throat. September–October. Clearings in conifer woods. Area 2 (endemic).

C. vallicola Herbert in *Bot. Reg.* 31, misc. 2 (1845)

Corm tunic thinly membranous-fibrous. Leafless at flowering time. Flowers white with long-tapering tips to the segments; throat white with 2 yellow spots at the base of each segment; anthers white; style three-branched, pale yellow. August–October. Alpine turf and subalpine pastures. Area 4 (and in Caucasus).

2 *Gladiolus* (Turkish: Kargasoğani)

Usually tall leafy plants having corms covered with fibrous tunics. Leaves linear, ensiform, distichous. Flowers in simple or branched spikes, usually pinkish-purple or pale to deep violet, zygomorphic with a curved tube; segments six, the upper median one usually larger than the rest, and rather hooded; lower median and lower lateral segments usually with a central patch of brighter or paler colour; stamens three, held just beneath the upper hooded segment; style slender, three-branched at the apex. Fruit a three-valved capsule with many winged or unwinged seeds.

This is a large genus of perhaps 120 species or more, the majority of which occur in South Africa and Tropical Africa. The Mediterranean and Asiatic species are generally much less colourful and smaller-flowered. The large-flowered garden cultivars of *Gladiolus* are hybrids between several South African species.

Although easily cultivated the Turkish species are seldom seen in gardens. Unlike the popular summer gladiolus hybrids of South African origin, they are hardy plants which can be grown in sunny situations and left in the ground permanently, not lifted for the winter as are their showy southern counterparts.

In Turkey there are about eight species, but the genus is in need of revision and they are not well-known at present.

G. atroviolaceus Boiss., Diagn. Pl. Or. Nov. Ser. 1, 13: 14 (1854)

Plant 35–70 cm tall. Leaves three with parallel veins, 4–8 mm wide. Flowers four to nine in a dense one-sided spike, deep violet-purple, 3.5–4.5 cm long. Dry slopes and in corn fields. April–May. Areas 2, 3, 8, 9, ?11, 12, ?13, 14, 15, ?16 (and widespread in Near East).

G. communis L., Sp. Pl.: 36 (1753)

This is often cultivated in its subsp. *byzantinus* (Miller) A. P. Hamilton, which is more vigorous than subsp. *communis*; in spite of its name, subsp. *byzantinus* probably does not occur in Turkey. Plant 50–100 cm tall. Leaves four to five, with veins diverging in the upper part, 1–2 cm wide. Flowers ten to 20 in loose, often branched, more or less two-sided spikes, reddish-purple, 3.5–5 cm long. April–May. Area 1. (Subsp. *communis* is widespread in S. Europe to Crimea.)

G. halophilus Boiss. & Heldr. in Boiss., Diagn. Pl. Or. Nov. Ser. 1, 13: 14 (1854)

Plant 25–45 cm tall. Leaves three, with parallel veins, usually 2–3 mm wide. Flowers two to six in a rather loose one-sided spike, 3–3.5 cm long, reddish-purple to bright pink. In steppe, usually on clay soils. April–May. Areas ?10, ?15, ?16 (and in Iran, N. Iraq, Transcaucasia).

G. illyricus K. Koch, Syn. Fl. Germ. ed. 2, 2: 806 (1844)

Plant 25–50 cm tall. Leaves with veins diverging in the upper part, 4–10 mm wide. Flowers three to ten in loose, more or less two-sided spikes, pinkish-purple or reddish-purple, 3–4.5 cm long. Stony places and dryish fields. April–May. Area 8 (and Mediterranean region and west Europe, north to Britain).

Var. *anatolicus* Boiss. was described as having narrower segments but this does not seem worthy of recognition.

G. imbricatus L., Sp. Pl.: 37 (1753)

Plant 30–80 cm tall. Leaves one to two with veins diverging in the upper part, about 7–15 mm wide. Flowers four to 12 in a short dense one-sided spike, violet or reddish-purple, 3–4.5 cm long. Damp meadows. April–June. Areas 4, 8, 13, 14, 15, 16, 18 (and widespread in east and central Europe).

G. kotschyanus Boiss., Diagn. Pl. Or. Nov. Ser. 1, 13: 15 (1854)

Plant 30–70 cm tall. Leaves two to three with veins diverging in the upper part, about 5–10 mm wide. Flowers four to seven in a dense one-sided spike, deep violet-purple, sometimes paler at the apex of the segments, 3–4 cm long. Damp meadows and in scrub. April–June. Areas 4, ?14, 15, 16 (and N. Iraq, W. Iran and Transcaucasia).

G. segetum Ker-Gawler in Bot. Mag. 19, t. 719 (1804)

Plant 40–100 cm tall. Leaves four to five, with veins diverging in the upper part, about 5–17 mm wide. Flowers five to 15 in a loose two-sided spike, pink or reddish-pink, 3.5–4.5 cm long. In fields. March–May. All areas of Turkey. It appears that this should now be named *G. italicus* Miller. *G. antakiensis* A. P. Hamilton is a similar but shorter plant (usually 20–60 cm) with only three to six flowers. Areas 8, 13, 18 (and in Lebanon).

G. tenuiflorus K. Koch in Linnaea 21: 636 (1848)
This was described from Şirvan in Siirt vilayet and from Bursa. It is a poorly known plant and in need of further study.

G. triphyllus Sibth. & Smith, Fl. Graec. Prodr. 1: 25 (1806)
Plant 10–35 cm tall. Leaves three to four, with veins more or less parallel, 2–4 mm wide. Flowers one to four in a loose one- or two-sided spike, pale to deep pink, 2.5–3.5 cm long. Rocky places and in light woods. April–May. Area ?8 (common in Cyprus).

3 Gynandriris

A small genus with a few species in South Africa and two in the northern hemisphere, one of which is widespread throughout the Mediterranean region and western Asia.

G. sisyrinchium (L.) Parl., Nuovo Gen. Sp. Monocot.: 49 (1854). (Syn: Iris sisyrinchium L.; I. maricoides Regel)
Plant 5–60 cm tall, with a subglobose corm covered by a coarsely netted tunic. Leaves two, basal, 0.5–10 mm wide, linear, channelled. Stem with terminal and lateral inflorescences, each two- to four-flowered. Flowers violet-blue or lavender-blue, white towards the base of the falls and with the blade somewhat spotted darker; sometimes there is a low yellow ridge in the centre of the falls; bracts membranous. Style splitting well above the base into three petaloid branches. Fruit a many-seeded, narrowly cylindrical capsule. March–April. Often in fields or cultivated areas and dry stony places. All areas of Turkey (and Mediterranean area eastwards to Pakistan and southwards to Arabia).

The garden value of this iris-like plant is slight since its flowers last only a few hours and are not showy. It may be of interest to the bulb enthusiast and should be grown in hot sunny places, or in a bulb frame where it can be ripened well.

4 Hermodactylus (English: Widow Iris; Turkish: Yumrulu süsen)

A monotypic genus but the one species is a common widespread plant in the central Mediterranean region, just extending into western Turkey. This extraordinary plant, with its green and brown iris flowers, is sometimes cultivated and is successful in sunny well-drained soils where its tubers become dry and warm in summer. Occasionally it is seen in florists' shops and, as a cut flower, the fragrance and curious colours can be appreciated.

H. tuberosus (L.) Miller, Gard. Dict. ed. 8 (1768). (Syn. Iris tuberosa L.)
Plant 20–40 cm tall, with a finger-like tuberous rootstock. Leaves four-angled in section, about 2–4 mm wide, longer than the flower stems. Flowers

solitary, yellowish-green with a deep brownish-violet blade to the falls. Standards about half as long as falls. Style branches petaloid. Ovary with one locule, ellipsoid with a short break. February–April. Dry rocky places. Area 6 (and in S. France, Italy, Balkans and N. Africa).

5 *Iris* (Turkish: Süsen)

This name is used for Iris of the bearded and non-bearded (Limniris) groups, depending upon the region of Turkey. People differentiate between wild and cultivated plants, the wild species being called *Ham* ('not ripe', or wild) and the cultivated ones *Has* ('genuine'). Thus the name *Ham Süsen* is used for certain wild species. For the Scorpiris (Juno) and Hermodacty-loides (Reticulata) groups there are separate names and these are given under the descriptions of these groups.

Plants with a rhizome or tunicated bulb. Leaves flat, canaliculate, angular or terete. Stem well-developed or obsolete. Bract and bracteole ('spathe valves') subtending one or more flowers. Flowers actinomorphic with six segments joined into a short to long tube; outer three segments ('falls') large, with a reflexed blade and usually with a signal patch of a more prominent colour in the centre for pollination purposes; inner segments ('standards') usually smaller and erect, sometimes reduced and horizontal or deflexed and rarely obsolete. Anthers three, extrorse. Style branches petaloid, each branch arching over the adjacent outer segment and carrying a stigma on its underside and bilobed at its apex. Fruit a three-valved capsule containing many flattened or subglobose seeds which are sometimes conspicuously arillate.

A genus of roughly 300 species, widespread in the northern hemisphere, especially in warm temperate areas. In Turkey there are about 40 species. They are mostly of great beauty and are popular garden plants. Surprisingly few of the Turkish species are in general cultivation although most are attractive. The best-known are the bearded irises, some of which are parents of the colourful garden cultivars, and the 'reticulatas' which are popular spring bulbs. The gaudy oncocyclus are seldom cultivated, requiring a hot, dry summer dormancy.

Iris can be conveniently divided into several subgenera, sections and subsections:

1. Plants with a rhizome; leaves flat, ensiform to linear   **2**
1. Plants with bulbs   **4**
2. Outer segments (falls) glabrous with no beard in centre   **3 Subgen. Limniris**
2. Outer segments bearded in the centre   **3**
3. Seeds with an aril; stem unbranched, with one terminal flower   **2 Subgen. Iris, Sect. Oncocyclus**
3. Seeds non-arillate; stem often branched, each branch more than one-flowered   **1 Subgen. Iris, Sect. Iris**
4. Leaves channelled; bulb tunics papery   **5 Subgen. Scorpiris**
4. Leaves square or terete in section; tunics netted   **4 Subgen. Hermodactyloides**

1 Subgenus *Iris*, Section *Iris* (Syn. *Pogoniris*; Turkish name: *Süsen*)

Plants with well-developed rhizomes. Leaves equitant, flat. Stem often branched, each branch usually more than one-flowered; falls with a beard in the centre; seeds non-arillate.

The bearded iris is cultivated in many Turkish gardens and is often planted in Moslem graveyards. The sword-like leaves pointing upwards are intended to drive away descending evil spirits and it is sometimes called the 'Flower of the Dead'. Some of the 'species' are known only from cemeteries and are probably ancient cultivars.

Records for *I. pumila* in Turkey almost certainly refer to *I. attica, I. schachtii* or *I. suaveolens.*

I. albicans Lange in *Vid. Meddel. Dansk Naturh. Foren. Kjφbenhavn* 1860: 76 (1861)

Plant 40–60 cm tall. Leaves ensiform, 1.5–2.5 cm wide, grey-green, straight. Flowers white, the branches of the inflorescence nearly sessile on the main stem; beard white tipped with yellow; bracts scarious in the upper half to two-thirds. April–June. Usually found near habitation, often in graveyards; introduced from Yemen and Saudi Arabia. It is probable that pilgrims (*Hadji*) returning from Mecca brought rhizomes of *I. albicans* and spread it through the East Mediterranean. *I. madonna* Sprenger is a pale blue form of the species, possibly a hybrid.

I. attica Boiss. & Heldr. in Boiss., *Diagn. Pl. Or. Nov.* ser. 2, 4: 91 (1859)

A very short species, stemless and only reaching to 10 cm when in flower. Leaves falcate, grey-green, 5–10 cm long and less than 1 cm wide. Flowers solitary, yellow with a brownish or purplish blade to the falls, or rarely bluish-purple throughout; beard yellow; bracts not or only slightly keeled. April. Rocky ground in scrub. Areas 2, 5 (and in Greece).

This species is very common in Greece where it occurs in several colour forms, yellow, white or purple or bicoloured combinations of these. The Turkish material differs slightly from the Greek in that its outer bract is sometimes keeled as in *I. suaveolens.* Cytologically, however, it appears to be closer to *I. attica* [see Sauer, W. and Leep, H. J.: 'Karyological investigations in Anatolian and S.E. European dwarf Iris Taxa (Iridaceae)' in *Pl. Syst. Evol.* 131: 81 (1979)].

I. biliottii Foster in *Gard. Chron.* 1887: 738 (1887)

Plant 60–80 cm tall. Leaves narrow at the base and widest just above the middle, 2.5–3 cm wide, more or less straight. Flowers bicoloured, the falls reddish-purple with brownish veins on a white ground in the lower part (haft); standards bluish-purple; beard yellowish; bracts long and narrow, green. April–May. Area 4 (endemic). Known only from graveyards in that area.

I. cypriana Foster & Baker in *Gard. Chron.* 1888: 182 (1888)

Plant 60–100 cm tall. Leaves ensiform, 2–3 cm wide, grey-green, more or less straight. Flowers very large, reddish-purple, standards paler; falls markedly wedge-shaped; beard white, bracts broad and rounded, the outer almost wholly scarious. April–May. Area ?7 (and in Cyprus).

I. germanica L. *Sp. Pl.*: 38 (1753).
Plant 60–100 cm tall. Leaves ensiform, 2.5–3.5 cm wide, grey-green, more or less straight. Flowers bicoloured, the falls dark violet with dark veining on a white ground in the lower part; standards paler bluish-violet; beard yellow; bracts scarious in the upper half to two-thirds. April–June. Usually in or near cultivated areas. Of unknown origin and naturalized in many European and Asiatic countries. 'Amas', 'Kharput' and 'Sivas' were collected in Turkey and are probably varieties of this.

I. junonia Schott & Kotschy ex Schott in *Österr. Bot. Wochenbl.* 4: 209 (1854)
About 20–45 cm tall. Leaves rather short compared to the other tall bearded Iris, being 30–40 cm long and 1.5–3.5 cm wide. Stem with several branches. Flowers yellow, whitish or lavender-blue, in the latter case the falls slightly darker and bluer than the standards; beard white tipped with orange; bracts green, scarious in the upper half. April–June. Area 8 (endemic).

I. mesopotamica Dykes, *Genus Iris*: 176 (1913)
Plant 90–120 cm tall. Leaves ensiform, up to 5 cm wide, green, only slightly glaucous, more or less straight. Flowers lavender-blue, the falls slightly darker than the standards; beard white tipped with yellow; bracts long and narrow, scarious in the upper third. April–May. Areas 8, 17, 18 (and in Syria, ?Lebanon, Israel).

I. purpureobractea B. Mathew and T. Baytop in *The Garden* 107, 11: 447 (1982)
Plant 20–40 cm tall. Leaves 1.5–2.5(–3.5) cm wide. Stem with two to four branches. Flowers pale blue with the falls suffused darker blue on the lamina and veined deep blue on the claw, or flowers wholly pale yellow with greenish-brown veining; beard yellow; bracts rather broad and inflated, obtuse or rounded, almost entirely suffused purple. Rocky places. April–May. Areas 5, 6 (endemic).

Related to *I. junonia* but can be distinguished by the inflated purple bracts and smaller flowers, with falls 6 cm or less long (in *I. junonia* they are 6–7 cm long).

I. schachtii Markgraf in *Gartenbauwiss.* 22: 550 (1957). (Syn. *I. lutescens* sensu Boiss., non Lam.)
Plant 10–20 cm tall. Leaves ensiform, more or less straight or slightly falcate, 0.8–1.7 cm wide, grey-green. Flowers purple or yellow with brownish veins; beard yellow; bracts scarious in upper part. May–June. Open rocky hillsides. Areas 5, 9, 10, 11, 12 (endemic).

Related to *I. taochia* but usually smaller with a narrower lamina to the falls and more strongly falcate leaves which taper more abruptly to the apex.

I. suaveolens **Boiss. & Reuter,** *Diagn. Pl. Or. Nov.* **ser. 1, 13: 15 (1853) (Syn.** *I. glockiana* **O. Schwarz,** *I. mellita* **Janka,** *I. rubromarginata* **Baker).**

Plant 5–15 cm tall. Leaves only 5–10 cm long, somewhat falcate, grey-green. Flowers solitary, reddish-purple or violet, or yellow with darker veining; beard yellow or bluish; bracts green, both strongly keeled. March–April. Areas 1, 2, 3, 5, 6 (and in Bulgaria, Yugoslavia and Roumania). The names var. *flavescens* Azn. and var. *violacea* Azn. were published to denote colour forms of *I. rubromarginata*.

I. taochia **Woronow ex Grossh.,** *Fl. Kavk.* **1: 256 (1928)**

Plant 25–30 cm. Leaves 1.5–2.5 cm wide, erect or slightly falcate, grey-green. Flowers purple or yellow; beard yellow; bracts scarious in upper part. May–June. Rocky hillsides. Areas 4, 14 (endemic).

I. trojana **Kerner ex Stapf in** *Verh. Zool.-Bot. Ges. Wien* **1887: 649 (1887)**

Plant 60–80 cm tall. Leaves 2.5–3 cm wide. Stem branched from low down, not just in the upper third as in most of the branched species, and sometimes with secondary flower clusters on the branches. Flower with reddish-purple falls and lighter bluish-purple standards; beard white tipped yellow; bracts narrow, tapering at both ends, scarious in the upper part. April–May. Areas 5, ?6 (endemic). Only known from graveyards in the area.

2 Subgenus *Iris*, Section *Oncocyclus* (Turkish names: *Kurtkulağı, Sultan Nevruzu, Eşek Nevruzu*)

Plants rhizomatous. Stem never branched, one-flowered; leaves equitant, often strongly falcate; falls with a beard in the centre; seeds with a large white aril.

The Oncocyclus Iris are probably the most striking of all Iris species in Turkey. The whole group is distributed in a limited area from central Anatolia eastwards to the Caucasus and Iran and south to Israel. They are easily recognized by their large gaudy solitary flowers on short stems, and their sickle-like grey leaves. They are well adapted to hot, dry conditions in summer and are consequently difficult to grow outside their natural habitat.

I. barnumae **Baker & Foster in** *Gard. Chron.* **ser. 4, 3: 182 (1888) forma** *barnumae*

Plants 10–25 cm tall. Leaves falcate, 1–7 mm wide. Flowers wholly purple, scarcely veined; beard yellow. May–June. Dry stony or sandy places. Areas 15, 16 (and in N. Iraq, and N.W. Iran).

Forma *urmiensis* (Hoog) B. Mathew & Wendelbo is similar in shape and size to f. *barnumae*, but the flowers are wholly yellow. April–May. Stony hills. Area 16 (and in N.W. Iran).

I. gatesii **Foster in** *Journ. Roy. Hort. Soc.* **11: 144 (1889)**

Plant 30–55 cm tall. Leaves suberect or slightly curved, usually 1–2 cm wide. Flowers very large, finely spotted and veined greyish or brownish on a white ground colour with a dark spot in the centre of the falls; beard greyish or brownish-purple. April–June. Rocky slopes and crevices. Areas ?4, 13, 17, 18 (and in N. Iraq).

I. iberica Hoffm., *Comm. Soc. Phys. Mosq.* 1: 41 (1806/8)

In Turkey represented by two subspecies:

Subsp. *elegantissima* (Sosn.) Fed. & Takht. Plant 15–30 cm tall. Leaves falcate, 2–6 mm wide. Flowers bicoloured, the falls heavily veined and spotted brownish-purple on a white ground with a round blackish or brownish spot in the centre; standards white with no veining or very slight veining towards the base; beard purple-brown. April–May. Rocky hill slopes. Areas 13, 14, 15 (and in N.W. Iran and adjacent Russia).

Subsp. *lycotis* (Woronow) Takht. is similar to the above, but has flowers with both falls and standards similarly coloured, heavily brown-purple veined on a pale ground. Area 16 (and in N.W. Iraq, W. Iran and adjacent Russia).

I. kirkwoodii Chaudhary in *Bot. Not.* 125: 499 (1972)

Plant (24–)50–60 cm tall. Leaves falcate, 5–8 mm wide. Flowers with falls coarsely spotted and strongly veined deep purple or violet on a whitish ground with a darker small round central blotch; beard purple-black or yellow; standards spotted and veined purple on a white or bluish ground, less prominently marked than the falls. April–May. Limestone hills, on stony slopes. Area 8 (and in Syria).

I. nectarifera Güner in *Notes Roy. Bot. Gard. Edinb.* 38, 3: 413 (1980)

Plant 25–53 cm tall. Leaves falcate, 9–13 mm wide. Flowers with falls strongly veined and flushed purple on a white or pale yellow ground, with a central blotch of deeper purple; beard yellow; standards whitish or pale yellow with slight purplish veining. April. In dryish steppe. Area 18 (endemic).

Var. *mardinensis* Güner has a slightly shorter perianth tube (2–2.5 cm) than the above var. *nectarifera* (3.5–4 cm) and often has narrower leaves 8–9 mm wide. Area 18 (endemic).

The similar *I. heylandiana* Boiss. & Reuter ex Boiss. from Iraq does not occur in Turkey.

I. paradoxa Steven in *Mém. Soc. Nat. Moscou.* 5: 355 (1817)

Plant 10–25 cm tall. Leaves strongly falcate, 2–4 mm wide. Flowers bicoloured and the falls smaller than the standards; falls nearly covered with a dense blackish-purple beard but with whitish markings at the apex and on the margin; standards much larger, white, veined with dark violet. April–June. Stony hill slopes and sandy areas. Areas ?14, 15, ?16 (also in N.W. Iran and S. Transcaucasia). The Turkish plant is forma *choschab* (Hoog) B. Mathew & Wendelbo. This is named after the castle of Hoşap (Güzelsu) near Van.

I. sari Schott ex Baker in *Gard. Chron.* 1876, 1: 788 (1876). (Syn. *I. lupina* Foster, *I. manissadjianii* Freyn)

Leaves falcate to suberect, 3–10 mm wide. Flowers heavily veined brown-purple on a white or yellowish ground, with a deep brownish-purple or maroon spot in the centre of the falls; beard yellowish. April–May. Stony hillsides. Areas 3, 8, 9, 10, 11, 12, 13, 17 (endemic). This species varies enormously in stature and flower size.

I. sprengeri Siehe in *Gard. Chron.* ser. 3, 36: 50 (1904). (Syn. *I. elisabethae* Siehe)

Plant 10–15 cm tall. Leaves falcate to suberect, 1–6 mm wide. Flowers whitish, strongly veined and streaked reddish-brown or purplish-brown and with a dark purple spot in the centre of the falls; beard yellow or cream. April–May. Dry stony places. Areas 8, 11 (endemic). *I. sprengeri* produces long stolons; it is closely related to *I. acutiloba* from Iran and the Caucasus.

I. susiana L., *Sp. Pl.*: 38 (1753)

Is sometimes cultivated in gardens. It is a robust plant with erect leaves 1–2 cm wide. The large flowers are densely veined and spotted blackish on a whitish ground colour. It does not occur wild in Turkey.

3 Subgenus *Limniris*, Section *Limniris* (Syn. *Apogon*; Turkish name: *Çayir suseni*)

Plants rhizomatous. Leaves equitant, flat, ensiform to linear. Stem usually well developed and sometimes branched. Flowers with glabrous falls and well developed standards.

I. kerneriana Asch. and Sint. ex Baker in *Gard. Chron.* 1: 795 (1884). (Syn. *I. graminifolia* Freyn)

Plant 25–50 cm tall. Leaves 15–30 cm long, narrowly linear, 2–5 mm wide. Flowers several in succession on a stem 20–40 cm tall, yellow. April–June. In scrub and grassy places. Areas 2, 3, 4, 5, 9, 11, 12, 13, 14 (endemic).

I. lazica Albov, *Prodr. Fl. Colch.*: 232 (1895)

Plant 12–25 cm tall. Leaves up to 25 cm long, broadly linear or ensiform, 0.8–1.5 cm wide. Flowers solitary, nearly stemless, pale to mid-violet with a yellow crest and a paler or whitish zone in the centre of the blade of the falls. February–March. On damp shady banks in woods at low altitudes. Area 4 (and in Black Sea area of Caucasus).

I. masia Stapf ex Foster in *The Garden* 61: 288 (1902) (Syn. *I. grant duffii* subsp. *masia* (Stapf ex Foster) Dykes)

Rhizome covered with reticulate tunics and old leaf bases which become very spiny. Plant 50–70 cm tall. Leaves up to 70 cm long, linear, 3–6 mm wide. Flowers solitary, on stems 40–60 cm tall, violet-blue with distinct veining on the falls. April–May. On plains and in fields. Areas 17, 18 (and in N. Iraq and Syria). *I. aschersonii* Foster is similar; it is said to have been collected by Siehe in Cilicia.

I. orientalis Miller, *Gard. Dict.*, ed. 8, no. 9 (1768). (Syn. *I. ochroleuca* L., *I. longipedicellata* Czeczott)

Plant 50–90 cm tall. Leaves 30–70 cm long, linear, 1–2 cm wide. Flowers several in succession, on stems to 80 cm tall, white with a yellow centre to the falls. April–June. Stream-sides, ditches and marshes. Areas 2, 3, 6, 7, 9, 11, 12, 13 (and in N.E. Greece).

I. pseudacorus L., *Sp. Pl.*: 38 (1753)

Plant 70–150 cm tall. Leaves 65–145 cm long, ensiform, 2–3 cm wide. Stem to 150 cm, branched, with one to two flowers in each pair of bracts. Flowers yellow with brown markings on the falls; standards only half as long as falls. In water or very wet places at low altitudes. Areas 1, ?2, ?3, 4, 5, 6, 7, 8, 10, 17 (and widespread in Europe and W. Asia).

I. sibirica L., *Sp. Pl.*: 39 (1753)

Plant 40–50 cm tall. Leaves about 40 cm long, linear, 5–8 mm wide. Flowers two to three, produced from brown papery bracts on stems about 30–40 cm tall, purple-blue with brownish veining on the falls. June–July. Wet meadows. Areas 3, 4, 14 (and in E. Europe and Russia).

I. sintenisii Janka in *Term. Füz.* 1, 4: 244 (1877)

Plant 10–30 cm tall. Leaves to 40 cm long, narrowly linear, 3–5 mm wide. Flowers two to several in succession, on stems 6–20 cm tall, deep blue-violet with paler streaking in the centre of the falls. June–July. Dryish rocky or grassy places and in scrub. Areas 1, 2, 5 (and in S. Europe).

I. spuria L., *Sp. Pl.*: 39 (1753)

Plant 40–80 cm tall. Leaves up to 50 cm long, linear, about 1–1.7 cm wide. Flowers one to several in succession on stems to 70 cm tall, pale to deep bluish-violet or creamy-white, sometimes bicoloured with the standards blue and the falls white; signal patch in the centre of the falls yellow. May–June. In salt marshes and streamsides. Areas 11, 12, 13, 14, 15, 16 (and in Iran and Caucasus).

The Turkish material represents subsp. *musulmanica* (Fomin) Takht.

I. unguicularis Poiret, *Voy. Barb.* 2: 86 (1789)

Plant 10–40 cm tall. Leaves 10–60 cm long, narrowly linear, 0.5–5 mm wide. Flowers solitary, nearly stemless but with a very long tube, lilac-blue, strongly veined in the centre of the blade of the falls; crest yellow. February–April. Dry sunny banks and stony places in maquis. Areas 6, ?7, 8 (widespread in the Mediterranean region).

Dwarf narrow-leaved forms are often called *I. cretensis* Janka but there is a gradation from one form to another.

I. xanthospuria B. Mathew & T. Baytop in *The Garden* 107, 11: 446 (1982)

Plant 50–100 cm in height. Leaves up to 70 cm long, linear, about 1–1.9 cm wide. Flowers several in succession, wholly golden yellow; standards well developed, as long as the falls. Stream-sides and marshy meadows at low altitudes. Areas 6, 8 (endemic).

Records for *I. x monnieri* DC. in Turkey almost certainly refer to this species.

4 Subgenus *Hermodactyloides* (Syn. *Reticulata*)

Turkish name: *Meşe nevruzu* (*Meşe* = *Quercus*; *Nevruz* = the Persian New Year, 22 March, indicating the flowering time and habitat of the Iris of this group).

Bulbous plants, the bulb covered with a netted tunic. Leaves basal, grey-green, one to three per bulb, quadrangular in section, or nearly cylindrical with eight ribs. Flowers usually solitary, with a stem or stemless, with a long perianth tube; standards erect and well-developed, or nearly absent.

I. bakeriana Foster in *Bot. Mag.* 115, t. 7084 (1899)
Usually 8–15 cm tall. Leaves 2–3 mm broad, eight-ribbed, appearing at flowering time but usually shorter than the flowers and elongating later. Flowers about 4–5 cm diameter, stemless, the falls mid blue with a darker violet blade and a white crest in the centre. Capsule erect, at ground level. March–April. Area 18 (and N. Iraq, W. Iran). The Turkish material is very distinct but in Iran the species merges with *I. reticulata*, with many intermediates.

I. danfordiae (Baker) Boiss., *Fl. Or.* 5: 124 (1884) (Syn. *I. amasiana* Bornm.)
About 4–6 cm tall. Leaves 2–4 mm wide, four-angled, about equalling the flowers at flowering time. Flowers small, about 3–4.5 cm diameter, stemless, yellow with greenish spotting on the falls; standards reduced to minute bristles. Capsule erect, at ground level. April. On partly wooded mountain slopes near snow. Areas 3, 4, 8, 12, 13, 14 (endemic).

I. histrio Reichb. il. in *Bot. Zeit.* 30: 488 (1872)
About 10–15 cm tall. Leaves 3–4 mm wide, four-angled, appearing before the flowers and overtopping them at anthesis. Flowers large, about 6–8 cm diameter, stemless, very pale blue with the falls prominently blotched all over with darker blue; crest yellowish. Capsule erect at ground level. January–February. In maquis. Areas 8, 17 (and in Syria, Lebanon and Israel).

In the Gaziantep and Maraş areas there is a small variety of this called var. *aintabensis* hort. It has flowers only 3.5–4.5 cm diameter, produced later, in April or May. The leaves are shorter than, or equal to, the flower at anthesis. It occurs in rocky places or fields.

I. histrioides (G. F. Wilson) S. Arnott in *Journ. Hort.* Ser. 3, 24: 121 (1892)
About 8–12 cm tall. Leaves 3–4 mm wide, four-angled, scarcely visible at flowering time but elongating rapidly as the flowers fade. Flowers large, about 5.5–8 cm diameter, stemless, mid blue with darker spots on the falls around the centre of the blade; crest yellowish. Capsule erect at ground level. March. In turf and bare ground among scattered pines in mountains. Area 3 (endemic to Ak Dağ, Amasya).

I. pamphylica Hedge in *Notes Roy. Bot. Gard. Edinb.* 23: 557 (1961)

About 20–30 cm tall. Leaves 2–3 mm wide, four-angled, about equalling the flowers at anthesis and becoming extremely long later. Flowers small, about 4.5 cm diameter, carried on a stem up to 20 cm long, bicoloured with the standards pale to mid blue and the falls deep purple with a yellow-orange crest. Capsule pendulous, held well above ground level. April. Edge of woods in scrub and among rocks. Area 7 (endemic).

I. reticulata M. Bieb., *Fl. Taur.-Cauc.* 1: 34 (1808)

Plant 6–15 cm tall. Leaves 2–4 mm broad, four-angled, appearing at flowering time but usually shorter than the flowers and elongating later. Flowers about 4–5 cm diameter, stemless, very variable in colour from bluish-violet to deep reddish-purple, the falls sometimes with a darker blade and with a yellow crest in the centre. Capsule erect at ground level. March–May. Alpine turf and hillsides, usually near snow. Areas 8, 13, 14, 15, 16, 17, 18 (and in N. Iraq, Iran, Transcaucasus).

Var. *krelagei* is the name given to the reddish-purple form from N.E. Turkey. An extremely variable species, in flower colour, size, amount of leaf development at flowering time and in the ability of the bulbs to produce bulblets.

5 Subgenus *Scorpiris* (Syn. *Juno*)

Turkish name: *Nevruz* or *Navruz* (the Iranian New Year, 22 March).

Bulbous plants, the bulb covered with papery tunics and usually with swollen or thickened roots. Leaves channelled, basal or alternate up the stem, which often elongates in the fruiting stage. Flowers solitary, or several produced in the axils of the upper leaves; standards usually much reduced and horizontal or deflexed. A group of about 50 species. Only one is in Mediterranean Europe; the rest are distributed from S.W. Turkey east to Israel, Iran, Caucasus, Afghanistan, Pakistan and Russian Central Asia.

I. aucheri (Baker) Sealy in *Kew Bull.* 1949: 562 (1949). (Syn. *I. sindjarensis* Boiss.)

Robust plant 15–40 cm tall. Leaves five to twelve, carried up the stem, 2.5–4.5 cm wide. Flowers three to six, pale to deep blue or white, produced in the axils of the upper leaves. March–April. Rocky places and ledges, or in fields. Areas 13, 15, 16, 17, 18 (and N. Iraq, N. Syria, W. Iran).

I. caucasica Hoffm. in *Comm. Soc. Phys. Mosq.* 1: 40 (1806/1808) subsp. *caucasica.*

Dwarf plant 15–20 cm tall. Leaves six to seven, basal at flowering time but later scattered up the elongated stem, 1–2 cm wide, ciliate on the margins. Flowers one to four, pale greenish-yellow or occasionally brownish, produced in the axils of the upper leaves. April–June. Stony slopes in mountains. Areas 4, 14 (and in Caucasus).

Subsp. *turcica* B. Mathew has the leaves smooth on the margins. It is more widespread in Turkey than subsp. *caucasica*. Areas 4, 9, 11, 12, 13, 14, 15, 16 (and N.E. Iraq).

I. atropatana Grossh. is probably synonymous with *I. caucasica*.

I. caucasica var. *kharput* Foster is a robust variant from the town of that name.

I. galatica Siehe in *Allgem. Bot. Zeitschr.* 1905: 115 (1905). (Syn. *I. purpurea* (hort.) Siehe, *I. eleonorae* Holmboe)

Plant 5–12 cm in height. Leaves three to four (to five), poorly developed at flowering time, expanding later to 0.6–1.2 cm wide. Flowers one to two, reddish-purple, greenish-yellow or more rarely pale silvery-purple, with a dark purple or violet blade to the falls. March–April. Rocky places in the open or in scrub. Areas 3, 4, 11, 12, 13 (endemic).

In *I. galatica* the two bracts are both green, not as in *I. persica* where the outer is rigid and green and the inner is thin, soft and semi-transparent.

I. persica L., *Sp. Pl.*: 40 (1753)

Dwarf plant about 10 cm tall. Leaves three to five, basal, falcate, only 0.5–1.5 cm wide. Stem nearly absent and not elongating in fruit. Flowers one to four produced at ground level, usually silvery-grey tinted with dull purple, often darker purple on the blade of the falls; sometimes the whole flower is a dull straw-yellow colour. February–April. Stony places and in sparse woods, mostly at low altitudes. Areas 8, 10, 11, 13, 17, 18 (and N. Syria, N.E. Iraq).

Several colour variants of this very variable species have been given specific names, including *I. bolleana* Siehe, *I. haussknechtii* Siehe, *I. issica* Siehe, and *I. sieheana* Lynch.

I. pseudocaucasica Grossh. in *Monit. Jard. Bot. Tiflis* 40–41: 11 (1916)

Dwarf plant 10–15 cm tall. Leaves four to six, basal at flowering time but later scattered up the elongated stem, 1–2.5 cm wide. Flowers one to four, yellow or pale blue, stemless or produced in the axils of the upper leaves. April–May. Rocky slopes. Areas 13, 15 (and N. Iraq, Iran, Transcaucasus).

Similar in general appearance to *I. caucasica* but the claw of the falls is winged and much wider than the blade. In *I. caucasica* the claw is the same width or only slightly wider than the blade.

I. stenophylla Hausskn. & Siehe ex Baker in *Gard Chron.* 1900, 1: 170 (1900) subsp. *stenophylla* (Syn. *I. tauri* Siehe ex Mallet; *I. heldreichii* Siehe)

Plant 6–12 cm tall. Leaves four to five, basal, poorly developed at flowering time, 0.5–1 cm wide at maturity. Flowers solitary, violet-blue or lilac-blue, stained a much darker blackish violet at the apex of the falls, with a whitish, violet-spotted, zone around the yellow or orange median crest. March–April. Rocky slopes. Areas 7, 8, 10, 11, 13 (endemic).

Subsp. *allisonii* B. Mathew differs in having six to ten leaves, 1.5–1.8 cm wide at maturity; the flowers are usually pale blue, very prominently blotched on the falls. Area 7 (endemic).

6 *Romulea*

Dwarf plants with a smooth tunicated corm with an oblique base. Leaves very narrow or thread-like, usually less than 1 mm wide, erect or coiling on the ground. Flowers funnel-shaped or starry when fully open, white, lilac, violet or yellow; perianth segments six, joined into a tube up to 1 cm long; stamens three, yellow; style slender, dividing into three bifid branches. Capsule oblong or globose, three-valved with many small globose seeds.

A large genus of about 70 species, mainly in South Africa but connecting through tropical African mountains to the Mediterranean region. In Turkey six species are recorded.

Most Turkish romuleas have rather small flowers and they are of little horticultural value, although easily cultivated. The most satisfactory way of growing them, to appreciate the crocus-like flowers at close quarters, is in a bulb frame or alpine house in pots.

R. bulbocodium (L.) Sebast. & Mauri, *Fl. Rom.* 17 (1818)
Plant 4–10 cm tall. Flowers usually pale lilac-blue with a yellow throat, 2–5 cm in diameter; tube up to 8 mm long. February–April. In pines or scrub at low altitudes. Areas 6, ?7, 8 (and widespread in Mediterranean region). A variable plant, sometimes white with purplish and green striping on the exterior; this is var. *leichtliniana*.

R. columnae Sebast. & Mauri, *Fl. Rom.* 18 (1818)
Plant 2–4 cm tall. Flowers white veined purple, only 5–7 mm in diameter; tube up to 5 mm long. March. Open stony places, in maquis and coastal sandy areas. Areas 6, ?7, 8 (and throughout Mediterranean region and W. Europe north to England).

R. crocea Boiss. & Heldr., *Diagn. Pl. Or. Nov.* Ser. 1, 13: 18 (1854)
Plant 4–8 cm tall. Flowers yellow with brownish stripes on the exterior, 2–4 cm diameter; tube up to 6 mm long. February–April. Sandy and stony places at low altitudes. Area 7 (? and Lebanon).

This is very closely related to *R. bulbocodium*.

R. linaresii Parl., *Fl. Panorm.* 1: 38 (1839)
Plant 2–4 cm tall. Flowers violet, greenish outside, about 1 cm diameter; tube up to 7 mm long. March. Open stony places and in maquis. Areas 1, 5, 6 (and Greece, Crete, Sicily).

R. ramiflora Ten., *App. Ind. Sem. Horti neap.* 3 (1827)
A vigorous plant, often with erect leaves up to 20 cm long, but flower stems much shorter. Flowers pale purple veined darker, sometimes greenish outside, about 1 cm diameter; tube up to 7 mm long. In the fruiting stage the stem elongates and shows clearly the branched scape. February–April. Sandy places. Areas 6, 8 (and widespread in Mediterranean).

R. tempskyana Freyn in *Bull. Herb. Boiss.* 5: 798 (1897)
Plant 3–10 cm tall. Flowers rich purple, greenish on the outside, about 2–3 cm diameter; tube 1 cm or more long. In clearings in scrub or pines. February–March. Areas 6, 7, 8 (and in other eastern Mediterranean countries, Cyprus).

SEVEN

Liliaceae

This is one of the largest of the families of petaloid monocotyledons. There are approximately 250 genera and probably as many as 3,700 species, spread throughout the world in all tropical and temperate regions. It is a very diverse family, ranging from small bulbous plants to shrubs, climbers and even trees. In Turkey, the Lily family is mainly represented by bulbous plants, but even so there is still great variation. At one extreme there are the spectacular and beautiful *Lilium* and *Tulipa* while at the other extreme are the dowdy small-flowered *Bellevalia* and *Muscari*. The genus *Allium* (onion, leeks, etc.) is also included here, although it is sometimes placed in a separate family, Alliaceae, because of the strictly umbellate inflorescence.

In addition to the species given below, *Erythronium dens-canis* has been recorded by Post[103] in the Belgrat Forest near Istanbul; it has not been re-collected there.

Family description

Herbaceous or evergreen, sometimes woody, perennials; rootstock a bulb or rhizome or rarely a tuber or a mass of fleshy roots. Leaves basal or cauline, linear, oval, or elliptical, sometimes thread-like and rarely cordate. In *Ruscus* the leaves are absent and are replaced by flattened leaf-like stems called 'cladodes'. Flowers regular, varying enormously in shape and size; they may be solitary or in long spikes, racemes or in umbels. Perianth segments six, separate or joined into a tube; in *Muscari* they are fused for most of their length and the six segments are reduced to small 'teeth'. Stamens six, often rather prominent. Ovary superior. Fruit a dry three-valved capsule or a fleshy berry.

Key to the 'bulbous' genera of Liliaceae in Turkey

1. Flowers erect and goblet-shaped or infundibuliform, produced at ground level **2**
   Flowers not as above **3**

2. Perianth segments joined into a long tube **4 *Colchicum***
   Perianth segments free **10 *Merendera***

3. Flowers produced strictly in terminal umbels; plant usually smelling of onions or garlic **4**
   Flowers not in umbels; no smell of onions **5**

4. Segments with three to five veins; flowers large, pendulous, campanulate on long pedicels **12 Nectaroscordum**
   Segments with one vein; flowers usually small and stellate, cup-shaped or ovoid **1 Allium**

5. Flowers erect and starry, yellowish or greenish, one to several in compact heads, not strictly umbellate, or rarely with one to a few small white campanulate flowers with purple veins **6 Gagea**
   Flowers not as above **6**

6. Leaves cauline, never strictly basal **7**
   Leaves basal, scape leafless **9**

7. Flowers campanulate or conical, pendulous **5 Fritillaria**
   Flowers infundibuliform, cup-shaped or flattish, sometimes with sharply recurved segments, erect or pendulous **8**

8. Leaves up to seven in number; flowers usually solitary, erect, flattish or cup-shaped at anthesis **16 Tulipa**
   Leaves ten or more; flowers usually more than one, erect to pendulous, infundibuliform or with recurved segments **9 Lilium**

9. Autumn flowering, flowers whitish; leaves produced later **17 Urginea**
   Spring- or summer-flowering, but if autumn-flowering, flowers blue; leaves present or withering at anthesis **10**

10. Flowers stellate, white with a green stripe on segments **13 Ornithogalum**
    Flowers stellate, tubular, cup-shaped, infundibuliform, globose or ovoid, usually blue, brownish or yellow **11**

11. Perianth segments free to the base **15 Scilla**
    Perianth segments joined into a tube, sometimes only shortly so **12**

12. Flowers constricted at the mouth, tubular, ovoid, obovoid or globose **11 Muscari**
    Flowers not strongly constricted at the mouth **13**

13. Flowers with a long tube, segments recurved, usually pale blue, very fragrant **8 Hyacinthus**
    Flowers with a short tube, companulate with spreading tepals **14**

14. Flowers with a small corona surrounding the stamens and style **14 Puschkinia**
    Flowers with no true corona **15**

15. Filaments exserted, flattened and held together, forming a white cone in the centre of the flower **3 Chionodoxa**
    Filaments included in the tube, very short and insignificant **16**

16. Leaves 2, with prominent fibre strands; flowers blue or violet; inhabiting dry rocky places **7 Hyacinthella**
    Leaves usually more than 2, without prominent fibres; fertile flowers usually brownish or dull purple; if blue, then plants of wet meadows **2 Bellevalia**

1 *Allium* (English: Onion, Garlic, Leek, Chives; Turkish: Soğan)

Biennial or perennial bulbous plants, usually with an onion or garlic-like odour and taste in the bulb and leaves. Bulbs solitary, or several clustered on a rhizome. Leaves basal or sheathing the stem, varying widely from filiform to cylindrical, flat, linear or elliptical. Inflorescence an umbel which may be spherical, hemispherical or fastigiate ('shuttlecock-shaped'), often many-flowered and at first enclosed within a spathe, pedicels with or without bracteoles at the base. Flowers stellate, cup-shaped, campanulate or ovoid with six free or partly-joined segments; segments one-veined. Stamens six, with the filaments connate at the base and fused to the perianth segments. Ovary three-locular, often with two ovules in each locule, but sometimes more. Stigma usually entire, rarely three-lobed. Seeds black, angular.

A large genus of perhaps as many as 500 species, distributed throughout the Northern Hemisphere and especially numerous in Europe and Western Asia. In Turkey there are probably about 100 species. Some species are commonly cultivated as vegetables and although not native to Turkey, are sometimes found in derelict areas of cultivation. These are *A. cepa* (Onion) and its various forms, *A. fistulosum* (Cibal), *A. sativum* (Garlic), *A. porrum* (Leek) and *A. schoenoprasum* (Chives). The latter is probably also native in Turkey. Some Turkish species are of ornamental value but the majority are not very showy and some are weedy when introduced to gardens, especially those which produce bulbils in the flower heads. Of the more attractive ones, the following are worth trying: *A. neapolitanum*, *A. roseum*, *A. nigrum*, *A. noeanum* and especially *A. akaka* which has broad flat leaves and nearly stemless heads. They require sunny well-drained positions.

Allium species, and the related *Nectaroscordum*, are sometimes placed in a separate family, the Alliaceae, and sometimes in the Amaryllidaceae. In flower structure however they agree with the characters of Liliaceae and it is more convenient here to retain them in that family.

The Turkish *Allium* species are numerous and many are not well-known at the present. It seems preferable in this book to describe a selection of species from each Section within the genus and list the names and places of publication of the others. Many other names can be found in literature and on herbarium specimens but many of these are synonyms or misidentific-ations. Until a thorough revision of the genus in Turkey is prepared, it is difficult to provide a reasonable guide to their identification.

The leaves and bulbs of some wild species such as *A. ampeloprasum*, *A. macrochaetum*, *A. rotundum*, *A. schoenoprasum*, *A. trachycoleum*, *A. vineale*, *A. zebdanense*, etc., are used locally under the names of wild onion or wild garlic. In the Van region, the scape and leaves of *A. vineale* (Turkish: Sirmo) are used, with some other herbs, in the preparation of a kind of cheese known as 'otlu peynir' ('cheese with herbs'). The bulbs of *A. ampeloprasum* and *A. macrochaetum* subsp. *tuncelianum* are used in the Tunceli and Adana regions under the name 'yabani sarımsak' (= wild garlic). In the Adana and Mersin regions *A. rotundum* is known as 'körmen' and its leaves are eaten. *A. zebdanense* leaves are used as food in the Taurus mountains where it is known as 'geyik körmeni'. *A. macrochaetum* is used instead of garlic in the Maraş and Adana areas under the name of 'kaya sarımsağı'. The fresh leaves of *A. schoenoprasum* are used in Van and Hakkâri instead of onions for flavouring.

In Turkey there are probably ten Sections of the genus *Allium* represented and these are lettered A to J below, with the species in each Section in numerical order. For identification purposes it is suggested that the reader first checks the Section descriptions to find out to which group the specimen in question belongs. The Sections are:

A Rhizirideum (page 53)
B Schoenoprasum (page 53)
C Scorodon (page 54)
D Allium (page 55)
E Codonoprasum (page 59)

F Molium (page 61)
G Porphyroprason (page 62)
H Acanthoprason (page 62)
I Melanocrommyum (page 63)
J Kaloprasum (page 64)

A. Section *Rhizirideum* G. Don ex K. Koch

Bulbs narrowly bottle-shaped, clustered on a rhizome. Leaves more or less basal or sheathing the lower part of the stem, flat. Flowers cup-shaped or bell-shaped. Ovules two in each locule of the ovary. Stigma not lobed at the apex.

1 *A. albidum* Fischer ex M. Bieb., *Fl. Taur.-Cauc.* 3: 260 (1819)

Clump-forming plant about 10–30 cm tall; bulb tunics tough, non-fibrous. Leaves erect, nearly basal, about 0.5–2 mm wide, linear. Umbel 1.5–2 cm diameter, hemispherical. Flowers starry or cup-shaped, white, yellowish-white or sometimes slightly tinged pink, with long-protruding stamens. July–September. Rocky places in mountains. Areas 4, 14 (and in S.E. Europe).

2 *A. saxatile* M. Bieb., *Tabl. Prov. Casp.*: 114 (1798). (Syn. *A. globosum* M. Bieb. ex Redouté)

Clump-forming plant usually about 10–35 cm tall; bulb tunics tough and dark brown splitting into strips. Leaves basal, filiform, only 0.5–1 mm wide. Umbel about 2–3.5 cm diameter, hemispherical, many-flowered. Flowers cup-shaped, deep pink or whitish, with protruding stamens. July–September. Rocky places and in steppe. ?Areas 3, 4, 14 (and in S.E. Europe).

3 *A. scabriscapum* Boiss. & Kotschy in Boiss., *Diagn. Pl. Or. Nov.* Ser. 1, 13: 31 (1854)

Clump-forming, about 12–50 cm tall, with leaves more or less basal, linear. Umbel hemispherical, 2.5–4 cm diameter, many-flowered. Flowers yellow with a green mid-vein on the segments. July–September. Rocky places in mountains. ?Areas 4, 13, 14, 15, 16 (and in Iran, Iraq and USSR).

Additional species, apparently belonging to this Section and recorded for Turkey:

A. szovitsii Regel in *Acta Horti Petrop.* 3, 2: 171 (1875).

B. Section *Schoenoprasum* Dumort

Bulb narrowly cylindrical or bottle-shaped, clustered on a rhizome. Leaves basal or sheathing the lower part of the stem, cylindrical or hollow. Flowers bell-shaped. Ovules two in each locule of the ovary, stigma not lobed.

1 *A. schoenoprasum* L., *Sp. Pl.*: 301 (1753)

Tufted plant, 10–45 cm tall. Leaves cylindrical, 2–5 mm wide, nearly basal. Umbel very dense, about 1.5–3 cm diameter, hemispherical or ovoid. Flowers lilac or pale purple-pink, bell-shaped, up to 1 cm long and often held more or less erect. Grassy mountain slopes or in rock crevices, over 2,000 metres. May–August. Areas 3, 4, 7, 13, 14, 15, 16 (widespread in N. Hemisphere).

C. Section *Scorodon* K. Koch (= Sect. Haplostemon (Boiss.) Hal., partly)

Bulbs ovoid or subglobose, not clustered on a rhizome. Leaves sheathing the stem, never basal, usually thread-like. Spathe two-valved, usually shorter than the pedicels. Flowers tubular to starry. Stamens with the filaments all untoothed or the three inner ones toothed (not with long pointed appendages as in Section *Allium*). Ovules two in each locule of the ovary. Stigma not lobed.

1 *A. anacoleum* Hand.-Mazz. in *Ann. Nat. Hofmus. Wien* 28: 17 (1914)

Usually 10–35 cm tall. Leaves filiform, inflated just above the base, only 0.5 mm wide. Umbel 1.5–2.5 cm diameter, hemispherical, many-flowered. Flowers purple with yellow at the base, bell-shaped. Mountain slopes. Areas 13, ?16 (and in Iran, N. Iraq).

2 *A. callidictyon* C. Meyer ex Kunth., *Enum. Pl.* 4: 413 (1843). (Syn. *A. lacerum* Freyn)

10–30 cm tall. Leaves filiform, less than 1 mm wide. Umbel loose, fastigiate with only four to nine erect flowers. Flowers white with a purplish-green nerve on each segment, narrowly bell-shaped; perianth segments sometimes laciniate in the upper part. Mountain steppe. ?Areas 3, 4, 12, 13, 14, 15, 16 (and in Iran, N. Iraq and Caucasus).

3 *A. capitellatum* Boiss., *Diagn. Pl. Or. Nov.* Ser. 1, 7: 118 (1846)

Plant 10–30 cm tall. Leaves filiform 0.5–1.5 mm wide. Umbel densely flowered, spherical, 1.5–2.5 cm diameter. Flowers bell-shaped, greenish-white or brownish-pink. Filaments exserted from perianth. Rocky places in mountains at high altitudes. Area 16 (and in Iran).

4 *A. cupanii* Rafin., *Caratt.*: 86 (1810)

About (5–)15–30 cm tall. Slender plant with a finely fibrous bulb tunic. Leaves filiform, only 0.5 mm wide. Umbel with rather few erect flowers which are carried on slender arching pedicels at anthesis. Flowers pale pink to purple with darker purple stripes on the segments. June–August. Rocky fields and stony hillsides. ?Areas 1, 3, 5, 6, 7, 8, 10, 11 (and in the Balkans).

5 *A. frigidum* Boiss. & Heldr. in Boiss., *Diagn. Pl. Or. Nov.* Ser. 2, 13: 34 (1853). (Syn. *A. achaium* Boiss. & Orph.)

This is a very similar to *A. moschatum* (see next species) but the bulbs are covered with papery tunics, not fibrous as in *A. moschatum*, and the pedicels are unequal. Area ?6 (and in Greece).

6 *A. moschatum* L., *Sp. Pl.*: 298 (1753)
Usually 15–25 cm tall. Bulb with fibrous tunics. Leaves filiform, about 0.5 mm wide. Umbel 1–3 cm diameter, fastigiate with 3–15 flowers on equal pedicels. Flowers pink or white with darker pink or brown central stripes on each segment. Dry grassy places. Areas 1, ?5, ?6, ?7, (and in S. Europe).

7 *A. sindjarense* Boiss. & Hausskn. ex Regel in *Acta Horti Petrop.* 3, 2: 121 (1875)
About 10–25 cm tall. Leaves filiform or narrowly linear, 1–3 mm wide. Umbel rather loose with unequal pedicels. Flowers bell-shaped, pink to purplish with a darker stripe on each segment. ?Areas 15, 16, 17, 18 (and in Iran, Iraq and Syria).
   Also recorded in Turkey and apparently belonging to this Section are:

A. alpinarii N. Özhatay & Kollm., in *Notes Roy. Bot. Gard. Edinb.* 41(2): 246 (1983) Area 8 (endemic).
A. brevicaule Boiss. & Bal., *Diagn. Pl. Or. Nov.* Ser. 2, 4: 119 (1859) Area 11 (endemic).
A. callimischon Link subsp. *haemastictum* Stearn in *Ann. Mus. Goulandris* 4: 154 (1978).
A. djimilense Boiss. ex Regel in *Acta Horti Petrop.* 3, 2: 108 (1875) Area 4 (endemic).
A. isauricum Huber-Mor. and Wendelbo in *Acta Hort. Gotob.* 28: 33 (1966).
A. peroninianum Azn. in *Bull. Soc. Bot. Fr.* 44: 175 (1897) Area 5 (endemic).
A. rubellum M. Bieb., *Fl. Taur.-Cauc.* 1: 264 (1808) (Caucasus).
A. sieheanum Hausskn. ex Kollm. in *Notes Roy. Bot. Gard. Edinb.* 41(2): 265 (1983) Areas 9, 10, 12 (endemic).
A. sivasicum N. Özhatay & Kollm. in *Notes Roy. Bot. Gard. Edinb.* 41(2): 266 (1983) Areas 11, 13 (endemic)
A. wendelboanum Kollm. in *Notes Roy. Bot. Gard. Edinb.* 41(2): 267 (1983) Area 18 (endemic).

D. Section *Allium* (= Sect. *Porrum*)

Bulbs ovoid or subglobose, not clustered on a rhizome. Leaves sheathing the stem, never basal. Spathe one- or two-valved, usually with a beak-like apex and falling off by flowering time. Flowers bell-shaped or egg-shaped with the segments connivent and partly closing the mouth of the flower. Stamens with the three inner filaments furnished with three to seven long-tapering appendages. Ovules two in each locule of the ovary. Stigma not lobed.

1 *A. affine* Ledeb., *Fl. Ross.* 4: 166 (1852)
This is rather like *A. phanerantherum* (see below) but the pedicels have bracteoles at the base (absent in the latter). ?Areas 7, 8 (and in Iran, Caucasus, Syria, Lebanon).

2 *A. amethystinum* Tausch in *Syll. Pl. Nov. Ratisbon.* 2: 256 (1828). (Syn. *A. descendens* Boiss.)
About 30–120 cm tall. Leaves linear, 5–15 mm wide, hollow, shrivelled at

flowering time. Umbel 3–5 cm diameter, nearly spherical, many-flowered, the outer flowers often on pendulous pedicels and the inner erect. Flowers purple, rather tubular. May–August. Rocky places in scrub or sparse woods. Areas 1, 5, 6, 7, 8 (and in S-C. & S.E. Europe).

3 *A. ampeloprasum* L., *Sp. Pl.*: 294 (1753)

About 30–150 cm tall. Leaves linear, 0.5–2 cm wide, rough on the margin, shrivelled by flowering time. Umbel 5–10 cm diameter, spherical, very dense and many-flowered or with bulbils and fewer flowers. Flowers pinkish or white, cup- or bell-shaped, the segments with obvious hair-like processes on the outside. May–July. Rocky or sandy places, often near cultivation. Areas 1, 3, 5, 6, 7, 8, 13 (and in Europe and W. Asia).

A. artvinense Miscz. ex Grossh. is a superficially rather similar plant, very robust with umbels 8–9 cm in diameter. Area 4.

A. bourgeaui Rech. fil. is rather similar but does not have hair-like processes on the outer segments. ?Area 6 (and in Aegean Is.).

4 *A. atroviolaceum* Boiss., *Diagn. Pl. Or. Nov.* Ser. 1, 7: 112 (1846)

About 40–100 cm tall. Bulb with clusters of small dark purple bulblets around it. Leaves linear, 3–8 mm wide. Umbel dense, spherical, 3–5 cm diameter. Flowers deep purple, cup-shaped. May–July. Dry grassy places and scrub. Areas 1, 2, 3, 4, 5, 6, 9, 14, 15 (and in Crimea, N. Iraq, Iran, Caucasus, Afghanistan).

5 *A. aucheri* Boiss., *Diagn. Pl. Or. Nov.* Ser. 1, 7: 116 (1846)

About 40–70 cm tall. Leaves nearly cylindrical, hollow. Umbel dense, many-flowered, spherical or hemispherical. Flowers tubular or bell-shaped, dark bluish-violet with a darker mid-vein on each segment. ?Areas 14, 15, 18 (and in Iran and Caucasus).

6 *A. caerulescens* Boiss., *Diagn. Pl. Or. Nov.* Ser. 2, 4: 115 (1859)

About 30–45 cm tall. Umbel very congested, about 1.5–3 cm diameter, the flowers on very short pedicels. Flowers dark violet-blue with a darker mid-vein on the segments. June–July. Grassy places in the mountains, and in pinewoods. Area 14 (?endemic).

7 *A. cappadocicum* Boiss. & Bal. ex Boiss., *Fl. Or.* 5: 241 (1882)

About 20–30 cm tall, very slender. Leaves very narrow. Umbel dense, spherical, many-flowered, about 1.5–3 cm diameter. Flowers pinkish-white. July. Sandy places. ?Areas 9, 10, 12 (endemic).

8 *A. guttatum* Steven in *Mém. Soc. Nat. Moscou.* 2: 173 (1809). (Syn. *A. margaritaceum* Sibth. & Smith)

About 15–50 cm tall. Leaves filiform, withered at flowering time. Umbel 1.5–3 cm diameter, nearly spherical and dense and many-flowered. Flowers whitish with a purple blotch on the segments. May–August. Dry grassy and stony places. Areas 1, 5, ?6, 7, ?8, 10, 11 (and in S.E. Europe).

A. guttatum subsp. *sardoum* (Moris)Stearn has a green or pink median stripe instead of a blotch on the segments. Area 1 (and in S. Europe).

A. gorumsense Boiss. is very similar to *A. guttatum*.

9 A. jubatum Macbride, Contr. Gray Herb. new ser. 56: 7 (1918). (Syn. A. cristatum Boiss.)

This is rather similar to *A. rotundum* (see below) but has the inner perianth segments toothed. Areas 2, 5 (and in Bulgaria).

10 A. longicuspis Regel in Acta Horti Petrop. 3, 2: 45 (1875)

About 40–110 cm tall. Leaves linear, 5–15 mm wide, flat. Umbel 2.5–4 cm diameter, ovoid, dense with many flowers and purplish bulbils. Flowers white or pink, ovoid with long-exserted styles. In mountain steppe. Area 16 (and in Iran and USSR).

This is similar to garlic, *A. sativum*.

11 A. phanerantherum Boiss. & Hausskn., Fl. Or. 5: 235 (1882)

About 25–85 cm tall. Leaves cylindrical, hollow. Umbel dense, spherical, 2–3.5 cm diameter. Flowers white with a green mid-vein on the tepals, or occasionally purplish. ?Areas 7, 8, 16, 17, 18 (and in Syria, Iraq and Iran).

Subsp. *deciduum* Kollm. & Koyuncu has a deciduous spathe. Area 8.

A. fuscoviolaceum Fomin is related to *A. phanerantherum* but has papillose pedicels (smooth in *A. phanerantherum*).

12 A. proponticum Stearn & N. Özhatay in Ann. Mus. Goulandris 3: 48 (1977)

This is rather similar to *A. sphaerocephalon* (see below) but is very robust and taller with a hemispherical umbel about 6.5 cm diameter. Rocky slopes. Area 1 (endemic).

A. proponticum var. *parviflorum* Kollm. has smaller perianth segments. Area 7.

13 A. rotundum L., Sp. Pl. ed. 2: 423 (1762)

About 30–80 cm tall. Leaves linear, 2–8 mm wide. Umbel 2–4 cm diameter, nearly spherical or hemispherical, very dense and tightly congested, but with no bulbils. Flowers ovoid, bicoloured, the outer segments deep purple and the inner paler pinkish-purple with a darker vein along the centre. May–July(-August). Dry grassy or waste places. Widespread in Turkey (and in Europe, Syria, Iraq, Iran and Caucasus).

A. calyptratum Boiss., recorded in Areas 8 and 10, is related to *A. rotundum* but has white flowers and a reddish spathe.

A. cilicicum Boiss. is like a small *A. rotundum*.

A. jajlae Vved. is similar to *A. rotundum* but the flowers are pink and the umbel is smaller (Caucasus).

W. T. Stearn considers *A. rotundum* and *A. jajlae* to be subspecies of *A. scorodoprasum*.

14 A. scorodoprasum L., Sp. Pl.: 297 (1753)

About 40–80 cm tall. Leaves linear, 5–15 mm wide. Umbel about 2–4 cm diameter with few flowers and many purplish bulbils. Flowers lilac to purple, ovoid. May–June. In scrub, waste places and grassy banks. Areas 1, 5, 9 (and in Europe).

15 *A. sphaerocephalon* L., *Sp. Pl.*: 297 (1753)

Plant 30–80 cm tall. Leaves semi-cylindrical, 1–5 mm wide. Umbel about 2–4 cm diameter, usually spherical and many-flowered, sometimes with bulbils. Flowers pink to reddish-purple, rarely white, rather tubular or ovoid; stamens much-protruding. June–August. Sandy and rocky places in grass and scrub. ?Areas 1, 5, 6, 7, 8 (and in Europe and N. Africa).

16 *A. trachycoleum* Wendelbo, in *Bot. Not.* 122: 35 (1969)

About 80 cm tall. Leaves linear, channelled, about 4 mm wide. Umbel 5 cm diameter, spherical, dense and many-flowered. Flowers campanulate or urn-shaped, white. Areas 8, 16 (and in Iran).

17 *A. vineale* L., *Sp. Pl.*: 299 (1753)

About 35–100 cm tall. Leaves cylindrical, 2–4 mm wide. Umbel very dense, 2–4 cm diameter, nearly spherical to hemispherical or ovoid, with or without bulbils. Flowers greenish or pinkish, campanulate. June–August. Grassy places and in waste ground. Widespread in Turkey (and in Europe).

18 *A. viride* Grossh., *Fl. Kavk.* 1: 201 (1928)

Plant 60–150 cm tall. Leaves cylindrical, hollow. Umbel dense, spherical, 2–4 cm diameter. Flowers green with a narrow white margin to the segments, ovoid. ?Areas 14, 15, 16 (and in N. Iraq, Iran and Caucasus).

A. baytopiorum Kollm. and N. Özhatay in *Notes Roy. Bot. Gard. Edinb.* 41(2): 246 (1983) is related but has larger segments which are scabrid. Area 14 (Ağrı Dağ) (endemic).

Other species recorded for Turkey and apparently belonging to this Section are:

A. armerioides Boiss., *Diagn. Pl. Or. Nov.* Ser. 1, 7: 116 (1846)

A. byzantinum K. Koch in *Linnaea* 22: 240 (1849) Area 5.

A. commutatum Guss., *Enum. Pl. Inar.*: 339 (1854) ?Area 6 (and in S. Europe).

A. dictyoprasum C. Meyer ex Kunth, *Enum. Pl.* 4: 390 (1843)

A. hamrinense Hand.-Mazz. in *Ann. Naturh. Mus. Wien* 28: 15 (1914) ?Area 8.

A. junceum Sibth. & Smith, *Prodr. Fl. Graec. Prodr.* 1: 226 (1806), and subsp. *tridentatum* Kollm., Koyuncu and N. Özhatay. Area 7.

A. karyeteini Post in *Bull. Herb. Boiss.* 3: 165 (1895)

A. macrochaetum Boiss. & Hausskn. ex Boiss., *Fl. Or.* 5: 239 (1882), and subsp. *tuncelianum* Kollm. Area 13 (endemic).

A. nevsehirense Koyuncu & Kollm. in *Israel Jour. Bot.* 27: 90 (1978) Area 11 (endemic).

A. pustulosum Boiss. & Hausskn. ex Boiss., *Fl. Or.* 5: 243 (1882)

A. reuterianum Boiss., *Diagn. Pl. Or. Nov.* Ser. 1, 5: 60 (1844)

A. robertianum Kollm. in *Notes Roy. Bot. Gard. Edinb.* 41(2): 264 (1983) Areas 7, 8 (endemic).

A. sandrasicum Kollm., N. Özhatay & Bothmer in *Notes Roy. Bot. Gard. Edinb.* 41(2): 264 (1983) Areas 6, 7 (endemic).

A. scabriflorum Boiss., *Diagn. Pl. Or. Nov.* Ser. 1, 5: 60 (1844)
A. stearnianum Koyuncu, N. Özhatay & Kollm. in *Notes Roy. Bot. Gard. Edinb.* 41(2): 266 (1983) Area 11, and subsp. *vanense* Kollm. & Koyuncu Areas 15, 16 (endemic).

E. Section *Codonoprasum* (Reichb.) Endl.

Bulbs ovoid, not produced on a rhizome. Leaves sheathing the stem, never basal. Spathe usually persistent (i.e. not falling off), two-valved, longer than the pedicels and with a wide, often strongly veined base and tail-like appendage at the apex. Flowers cup-shaped or tubular, not starry. Stamens with simple, not toothed, filaments. Ovules two in each locule of the ovary. Stigma not lobed.

1 *A. armenum* Boiss. & Kotschy ex Boiss., *Fl. Or.* 5: 254 (1882)

Small plant 5–15 cm tall. Leaves linear. Umbel rather loose, spherical, 2–3 cm diameter. Flowers mid to deep purple. May–August. Rocky places up to 3,000 metres. Areas, 8, 13, 14, 17 (endemic).

   A. huber-morathii Kollm., N. Özhatay & Koyuncu is similar but the spathes overtop the umbel and the flowers are purplish-pink. Areas 2, 9 (endemic).

   A. tchihatchewii Boiss. seems also to be very similar to *A. armenum*.

2 *A. chlorurum* Boiss. & Hausskn. ex Boiss., *Fl. Or.* 5: 264 (1882). (Syn. *A. tauricolum* Boiss.)

Small plant about 4–6 cm tall. Leaves linear. Umbel 1.5–2 cm diameter, hemispherical. Flowers violet with a dark vein along each segment. August. Rocky places in mountains. Areas 7, 8 (endemic).

3 *A. flavum* L., *Sp. Pl.*: 298 (1753). (Syn. *A. guicciardii* Heldr., *A. webbii* Clementi)

About 5–30 cm tall. Leaves cylindrical, grey-green, about 1–2 mm wide. Umbel 1.5–3 cm diameter, loose, few to many-flowered, the inner flowers on upright stalks, the outer curving downwards. Flowers pale to deep yellow, campanulate, with the segments more than 5 mm long. June–August. Dry grassy places. Areas 1, 5, 7, 16 (and in S. Europe).

4 *A. kunthianum* Vved. in *Fl. URSS* 4: 207 (1935)

Plant 15–25 cm tall. Leaves very narrow, 0.5–1 mm wide, channelled, very strongly ribbed. Umbel fastigiate or hemispherical, rather dense, about 1.5–2 cm diameter. Flowers narrowly campanulate, pale pink with purple mid-veins on the segments. ?Areas 4, 14, 15 (and in Iran and Caucasus).

5 *A. melanantherum* Pancić, *Elem. Fl. Bulg.*: 64 (1883). (Syn. *A. thracicum* Halacsy & Georg.)

About 15–40 cm tall. Leaves filiform. Umbel loose, fastigiate, often with a few bulbils, about 1.2–5 cm diameter. Flowers pink with a reddish mid-vein on the segments, cylindrical. Grassy places. ?Area 1 (and in Balkans).

6 *A. myrianthum* Boiss., *Diagn. Pl. Or. Nov.* Ser. 1, 5: 59 (1844)

Plants 25–75 cm tall. Leaves 1–2.5 mm wide, semi-cylindrical, channelled and hollow in the lower part. Umbel dense, spherical, 2–4 cm diameter. Flowers small, white, campanulate. May–June. Rocky places. Areas 1, 6, 7, 8, 13, 17 (and in Iraq and Iran).

7 *A. pallens* L., *Sp. Pl.* ed. 2: 427 (1762). (Syn. *A. coppoleri* Tineo)

About 10–40 cm tall. Leaves filiform, 0.5–3 mm wide. Umbel compact, 1.5–3.5 cm diameter, hemispherical or fastigiate; pedicels only 5–15 mm long. Flowers white or pink, narrowly campanulate. May–July. Dry grassy places and in scrub. Areas 1, 5, 6, 7, 8 (and in S. Europe).

8 *A. paniculatum* L., *Syst. Nat.* ed. 10, 2: 978 (1759). (Syn. *A. fuscum* Waldst. & Kit.)

Leaves narrowly linear with glabrous sheaths. Umbel 1.5–3 cm diameter, rather loose, fastigiate, hemispherical or ovoid, many-flowered with the outer flowers pendulous on long pedicels. Flowers usually pinkish, often with darker mid-veins. Stamens not or scarcely exserted. June–October. Dry grassy or stony places. Widespread in Turkey (and in S. Europe, Iraq and Iran).

Subsp. *fuscum* (Waldst. & Kit.) Arcang. has brownish or dirty yellow flowers.

Subsp. *villosulum* (Hal.) Stearn (Syn. *A. rhodopeum* Velen.) has hairy leaf sheaths. ?Areas 1 (and Bulgaria).

The little known *A. karsianum* Fomin is rather similar to *A. paniculatum*.

9 *A. rupestre* Steven in *Mém. Soc. Nat. Moscou* 3: 260 (1812)

This is rather like *A. pallens* (see above) but has purple anthers (yellow in *A. pallens*). ?Area 3 (and in Crimea and Caucasus).

10 *A. sipyleum* Boiss., *Diagn. Pl. Or. Nov.* Ser. 1, 5: 58 (1844)

This looks like a dwarf, few-flowered *A. paniculatum*, usually only about 10–25 cm tall. ?Area 7 (and in Greece).

11 *A. stamineum* Boiss., *Diagn. Pl. Or. Nov.* Ser. 2, 4: 119 (1859). (Syn. *A. amphipulchellum* Zahar.)

Plant 5–25 cm tall. Leaves filiform, only 0.5–1 mm wide. Umbel 2.5–5 cm diameter, many-flowered, but rather loose, more or less spherical or fastigiate. Flowers cup-shaped, pale pinkish-purple with darker mid-veins on the perianth segments. Stamens much exserted. May–July. Dry grassy or stony places. Widespread in Turkey (and in Balkans, Iraq and Iran).

A. kossoricum Fomin is probably a synonym.

12 *A. staticiforme* Sibth. & Smith, *Fl. Graec. Prodr.* 1: 225 (1809)

About 10–30 cm tall. Leaves filiform, hollow. Umbel 1.5–2.5 cm diameter, hemispherical, dense. Flowers obovoid, pink with red mid-veins on the segments; sometimes whitish. Sandy areas near the sea. Area 1 (and in S. Greece).

A. kurtzianum Asch. & Sint. ex Kollm. is similar but usually shorter and has spathes which are not abruptly contracted like those of *A. staticiforme*. Area 5.

13 *A. carinatum* L., *Sp. Pl.*: 297 (1753)

About 30–60 cm tall. Leaves linear, 1–2.5 mm wide. Umbel loose with the outer flowers pendulous and bulbils present as well. Flowers purple, campanulate, with the segments 4–6 mm long, blunt; stamens protruding. Areas 1, 5, ?6 (and in S. and C. Europe).

Subsp. pulchellum Bonnier & Layens has no bulbils and more flowers in the umbel; it is probably not in Turkey (S. Europe).

Other species recorded for Turkey and apparently belonging to this Section are:

A. bassitense J. Thiébaut in *Bull. Soc. Bot. Fr.* 95: 20 (1948) Area 8.

A. deciduum N. Özhatay & Kollm, in *Notes Roy. Bot. Gard. Edinb.* 41(2): 246 (1983). Subsp. *deciduum*. Areas 6, 7; Subsp. *retrorsum*. Area 8 (endemic).

A. glumaceum Boiss. & Hausskn. ex Boiss., *Fl. Or.* 5: 260 (1882) Area 8.

A. hirtovaginum Candargy, in *Bull. Soc. Bot. Fr.* 44: 142 (1897) Area 8 (and in Greece).

A. kastambulense Kollm. in *Notes Roy. Bot. Gard. Edinb.* 41(2): 248 (1983) Area 2 (endemic).

A. montanum Sibth. & Smith, *Fl. Graeca* 4: 17, t. 319 (1823)

A. olympicum Boiss., *Diagn. Pl. Or. Nov.* Ser. 1, 5: 58 (1844)

A. phrygium Boiss., *Fl. Or.* 5: 256 (1882)

A. rupicolum Boiss. ex Mout. in *Nouv. Fl. Liban et Syrie* 1: 273 (1966)

A. subquinqueflorum Boiss., *Fl. Or.* 5: 264 (1882)

A. variegatum Boiss., *Diagn. Pl. Or. Nov.* Ser. 1, 7: 118 (1846)

A. wiedemannianum Regel in *Acta Horti Petrop.* 3, 2: 199 (1875)

F. Section *Molium* G. Don ex K. Koch.

Bulbs ovoid or subglobose, not produced on a rhizome. Leaves basal, flat. Flowers starry or bell-shaped; segments not reflexing after flowering and not becoming rigid and spiny. Ovules two in each locule of the ovary. Stigma not lobed.

1 *A. eriophyllum* Boiss., *Diagn. Pl. Or. Nov.* Ser. 1, 7: 112 (1846)

About 10–60 cm tall. Leaves narrowly linear-lanceolate, usually about 5–10 mm wide, long-acuminate. Umbel hemispherical or rather fastigiate. Flowers pink, campanulate, with the segments 1–1.5 cm long, acuminate at the apex. Areas 15, 16 (and in Syria, Iraq and Iran).

A. laceratum Boiss. & Noë is like *A. eriophyllum* but has the segments laciniate at the apex. *Flora Iranica* treats it as a variety of *A. eriophyllum*. ?in S.E. Turkey (and in Syria, Iraq and Iran).

2 *A. neapolitanum* Cirillo, *Pl. Rar. Neap.* 1: 13 (1788)

About 20–45 cm tall. Leaves usually only 2–3, linear, 1–2 cm wide. Umbel 5–9 cm diameter, hemispherical, many-flowered. Flowers large, up to 2 cm diameter, white, cup-shaped or stellate. March–April. Dry grassy or stony places. ?Areas 1, 5, 6, 7, 8 (and in S. Europe).

3 *A. roseum* L., *Sp. Pl.*: 296 (1753)

About 15–55 cm tall. Leaves linear, varying from almost thread-like to 1.5 cm wide. Umbel 4–7 cm diameter, fastigiate or hemispherical, with or without bulbils. Flowers large, pink or white, broadly cup-shaped. April–June. Fields and grassy places at low altitudes. ?Areas 1, 5, 6, 7, 8 (and in S. Europe).

4 *A. subhirsutum* L., *Sp. Pl.*: 295 (1753)

Slender plant, 10–30 cm tall. Leaves linear, usually 2–7 mm wide, ciliate. Umbel 3–6 cm diameter, loose and hemispherical. Flowers white, flat and stellate. April–June. Dry stony and sandy places. ?Areas 1, 5, 6, 7, 8 (and in S. Europe).

Also recorded for Turkey and apparently belonging to this Section are:

A. cassium Boiss., *Diagn. Pl. Or. Nov.* Ser. 1, 13: 28 (1853)
A. gayi Boiss., *Fl. Or.* 5: 271 (1882)
A. hirsutum Zucc., in *Abh. Bayr. Acad.* 3: 232 (1843)
A. papillare Boiss., *Diagn. Pl. Or. Nov.* Ser. 1, 13: 27 (1853)
A. zebdanense Boiss. & Noë, *Diagn. Pl. Or. Nov.* Ser. 2, 4: 113 (1859)

G. Section *Porphyroprason* Ekberg

Bulbs globose, not clustered on a rhizome, producing stalked bulbils. Scape very short with leaves sheathing, but appearing basal or nearly so because of the partly subterranean stem. Leaves flat in vernation (i.e. pressed flat against each other at the base). Flowers broadly bell-shaped. Stigma three-lobed.

1 *A. balansae* Boiss., *Fl. Or.* 5: 268 (1882)

Only 5–8 cm tall. Leaves filiform, shorter than the flower stem. Umbel dense, spherical, 1.5–2 cm diameter. Flowers deep lilac-pink. August. In mountain turf. Areas 3, 5 (endemic).

2 *A. oreophilum* C. Meyer, *Verz. Pfl. Cauc.*: 37 (1831). (Syn.: *A. ostrowskianum* Regel)

About 5–15 cm tall. Leaves two, linear, 2–8 mm wide, grey-green. Umbel 2–4 cm diameter, few-flowered, hemispherical. Flowers large, broadly campanulate, rose-purple, about 1–1.5 cm diameter. July. In scree, up to 3,500 metres altitude. Area 15 (and in Afghanistan, Pakistan, Caucasus and Russian Middle Asia).

H. Section *Acanthoprason* Wendelbo

Bulbs ovoid or globose, not produced on a rhizome. Leaves basal, convolute in vernation (i.e. wrapped around each other at the base). Flowers flattish, the perianth segments becoming rigid and almost spiny after flowering.

1 *A. akaka* Gmelin in Roem. & Schultes, *Syst. Veg.* 7: 1132 (1830)

Usually 5–15 cm tall. Leaves 1 or 2, grey-green, 2–6 cm wide, elliptic-oblong, often flat on the ground. Umbel 4–7 cm diameter, hemispherical, many-flowered, often nearly stemless. Flowers broadly campanulate or stellate, rose-pink or purplish, becoming spiny after anthesis. June–July. Dry rocky slopes in mountains. Areas 13, 14, 15, 16 (and in Iran and Caucasus).

2 *A. haemanthoides* Boiss. & Reuter ex Regel, *Acta Horti Petrop.* 3, 2: 240 (1875)

This is very like *A. akaka* and may only be a variant of it. The segments are 9–15 mm long (less than 9 mm in *A. akaka*). Possibly occurring in Area 16 (and in Iran).

I. Section *Melanocrommyum* Webb. & Berth

Bulbs subglobose, not clustered on a rhizome. Leaves basal. Spathes shorter than the pedicels, splitting into two to four parts and persisting. Flowers starry with the segments usually reflexed after flowering. Stamens with simple, not toothed, filaments. Ovules four to eight in each locule. Stigma not lobed.

1 *A. atropurpureum* Waldst. & Kit., *Pl. Rar. Hung.*, 1: 16 (1800)

Usually 40–100 cm tall. Leaves broadly linear, 1–4 cm wide. Umbel 4–6 cm diameter, broadly fastigiate, many-flowered. Flowers deep red-purple, flat and stellate. May–June. Dryish places, in grass or scrub. Areas 1, 5 (and in Balkans).

2 *A. cardiostemon* Fischer & C. Meyer, *Ind. Sem. Hort. Petrop.* 6: 43 (1840). (Syn. *A. trilophostemon* Bornm.)

Usually 15–40 cm tall. Leaves two to three, narrowly linear. Umbel many-flowered, dense, 2–3 cm diameter, broadly fastigiate. Flowers deep blackish-maroon. June–July. Rocky slopes and alpine meadows. Areas 8, 13, 14, 15, 16 (and in Iran and Caucasus).

3 *A. chrysantherum* Boiss. & Reuter in Boiss., *Fl. Or.* 5: 280 (1882)

About 30–100 cm tall. Leaves several, linear-lorate, 1–1.5 cm wide, often undulate. Umbel broadly fastigiate, about 3–5 cm diameter with many flowers. Flowers greenish-yellow or yellow with a blackish ovary. April–June. Rocky slopes and scree. Areas 13, 16, ?18 (and in Syria, Iraq and Iran).

4 *A. colchicifolium* Boiss., *Diagn. Pl. Or., Nov.* Ser. 2, 4: 112 (1859)

Plant 5–20 cm tall. Leaves one to two, elliptic or suborbicular, up to 12 cm broad. Umbel hemispherical, 3–5 cm diameter, dense and many-flowered. Flowers broadly campanulate, whitish or green with darker mid-veins on the segments. May. Areas 17, 18 (and in Iraq and Iran).

**5 *A. decipiens* Fischer ex Schultes & Schultes fil., *Syst. Veg.*
7: 1117 (1830)**

Plant 20–50 cm tall. Leaves one to three, linear, 2–10 mm wide. Umbel about 2.5–5 cm diameter, hemispherical or broadly fastigiate. Flowers stellate, pale pinkish-purple or whitish, the segments reflexed after anthesis. June. Rocky slopes. Probably occurring in N. Turkey (and in S. Russia).

**6 *A. kharputense* Freyn & Sint. in *Österr. Bot. Zeitschr.* 42:
378 (1982)**

About 30–45 cm tall. Leaves usually two to four, lanceolate, 2–3 cm wide, erect and twisted. Umbel broadly fastigiate, many-flowered, about 3–5 cm diameter. Flowers white with a blackish-green or dark red ovary, stellate. May. In fields and dry stony places. Areas 12, 13, 14, 15, 17, 18 (and in Iran).

7 *A. nigrum* L., *Sp. Pl.* ed. 2: 430 (1762)

About 55–80 cm tall. Leaves two to three, broadly linear, about 2.5–4.5 cm wide, long-tapering at the apex. Umbel usually 6–8 cm diameter, hemispherical or fastigiate, many-flowered, occasionally with some bulbils. Flowers white or pale pink with a green mid-vein on each segment, stellate but the segments reflexing after anthesis. Ovary dark green or blackish. April–June. Usually in or near cultivated land. ?Areas 1, 5, 6, 7, 8 (and in S. Europe).

**8 *A. noeanum* Reuter ex Regel in *Acta Horti Petrop.* 3, 2: 235
(1875)**

Plant 20–30 cm tall. Leaves three to four (to seven), lorate, 2–4 cm wide. Umbel fastigiate, 5–12 cm diameter. Flowers lilac-pink to deep pink with narrow, acute segments, campanulate at anthesis. May–June. In fields and edges of cultivated land. Area 17 (and in Syria, Iraq and Iran).

9 *A. orientale* Boiss., *Diagn. Pl. Or. Nov.* Ser. 2, 13: 25 (1853)

About 10–40 cm tall. Leaves three to four, narrowly lanceolate or linear, 0.5–2 cm wide. Umbel 3–5 cm diameter, hemispherical, many-flowered. Flowers stellate, white with a green mid-vein on the segments, which do not reflex after anthesis. April–June. Sparse woodland and grassy places. ?Areas 5, 6, 7, 8 (and in E. Aegean).

Also recorded from Turkey and apparently belonging to this Section are:

A. aschersonianum Barbey, *Herb. Levant* 163, t. 4 (1882)

A. cyrilli Ten., *Fl. Nap.* 3: 364 (1828–9) Areas ?1, 5 (and in S. Greece and S. Italy).

A. hirtifolium Boiss., *Fl. Or,* 5: 281 (1882) Area 15 (and in Iran).

A. karamanoglui Koyuncu & Kollm. in *Israel Jour. Bot.* 29: 93 (1978)
Area 8

A. lycaonicum Siehe in *Ann. Nat. Hofmus. Wien.* 28: 185 (1914)

A. rothii Zucc., in *Abh. Bayer. Akad.* 3: 232 (1843)

A. stenopetalum Boiss. & Kotschy ex Regel in *Acta Horti Petrop.* 3,
2: 231 (1875)

J. Section *Kaloprasum* K. Koch

Bulbs subglobose, not clustered on a rhizome. Leaves basal. Spathe two-valved, shorter than the pedicels, persistent. Flowers bell-shaped, the segments not reflexing or becoming spiny after flowering. Stamens with simple, not toothed, filaments. Ovules six to eight in each locule. Stigma not lobed.

1 *A. schubertii* Zucc. in *Abh. Bayer. Akad*. 3 : 234 (1843)
Usually 10–25 cm tall. Leaves two to four, about 1–5 cm wide. Umbel very large, spherical, many-flowered but lax; pedicels extremely unequal, up to 20 cm long. Flowers pale brown with a darker vein on each tepal, broadly campanulate at anthesis but the segments becoming erect later. This very distinctive plant possibly occurs in Areas 17 or 18 (and in E. Mediterranean).

Other less well-known *Allium* species, which have at some time been recorded in Turkey, are as follows. It is not always clear to which Section they belong, nor is it definite that they all occur in Turkey. Some records for species may merely be a case of misidentification in the past.

A. albo-tunicatum O. Schwarz in *Feddes Repert.* 36 : 73 (1934)
A. asclepiadeum Bornm. in *Notizbl. Bot. Gart. Berlin* 7 : 42 (1917)
A. eginense Freyn in *Mem. Herb. Boiss.* 13 : 34 (1900)
A. filifolium Freyn & Sint. in *Österr. Bot. Zeitschr.* 44 : 392 (1894)
A. fimbriatum Schischkin in *Ber. Tomsk. Staats. Univ.* 81 : 432 (1928)
A. janthinum Freyn in *Bull. Herb. Boiss.* 4 : 191 (1896)
A. ledschanense Conrath & Freyn in *Bull Herb. Boiss.* 4 : 190 (1896)
A. microspathum Ekberg in *Bot. Not.* 122 : 20 (1969)
A. pictistamineum O. Schwarz in *Fedde, Repert.* 36 : 72 (1934)
A. ponticum Miscz. ex Grossh., *Fl. Kavk.* 1 : 206 (1928). Area 4.
A. rhetoreanum Náb. in *Publ. Fac. Sci. Univ. Masaryk*, Brno 105 : 38 (1929)
A. rollovii Grossh., *Fl. Kavk.* 1 : 205 (1928) Area 4.
A. sibthorpianum Schultes, *Syst. Veg.* 7, 2 : 1057 (1830)
A. sintenisii Freyn in *Österr. Bot. Zeitschr.*, 42 : 377 (1892)
A. stylosum O. Schwarz in *Feddes Repert.* 36 : 71 (1934)
A. tmoleum O. Schwarz in *Feddes Repert.* 36 : 71 (1934)
A. tristiasimum Freyn & Sint. in *Österr. Bot. Zeitschr.* 44 : 393 (1894)
A. tubergenii Freyn in *Mem. Herb. Boiss.* 13 : 32 (1900)
A. woronowii Miscz. ex Grossh., *Fl. Kavk.* 1 : 217 (1928) Area 15.

2 *Bellevalia*

A genus of about 50 species, rather dull in their flower colour except for the blue-flowered *B. pycnantha*, *B. paradoxa* and *B. forniculata*. They have large, tunicated bulbs, basal strap-shaped or lanceolate leaves and long racemes of flowers. The flowers are campanulate with a short to long perianth tube and six lobes with the stamens attached just inside the mouth of the perianth. Fruit a three-valved capsule with large smooth globose seeds which are covered with a waxy 'bloom'.

In Turkey 17 species have been recorded. For more information see Feinbrun in *Palestine Journal of Botany*, Jerusalem series Vol. 1, no. 1, p. 42

(1939). They flower in April to July and usually occur in fields and on open hillsides. The ornamental value of these muscari-like plants is almost nil, except perhaps for the blue-flowered species which are at present little-known in gardens. One of these, *B. forniculata*, is dwarf and of an intense blue colour so it will probably be of interest to rock gardeners when available.

B. aucheri (Baker) Feinbr. in *Pal. Journ. Bot. Jerusalem Ser.* 1, 2: 353 (1939)

Leaves three per bulb, about 1.8 cm wide, with a scabrid margin. Raceme many-flowered, dense at first. Pedicels about 1–2.5 cm long at flowering time, elongating rapidly in fruit. Flowers 1–1.2 cm long, brownish, the lobes about equal to or slightly shorter than the tube. Area 8 (?endemic).

The original specimen was said to have been collected in Iran but this was probably a mistake.

Feinbrun cited *B. longipes* Post as occurring in Turkey but the specimen concerned represents *B. aucheri*.

B. clusiana Griseb., *Spicil. Fl. Rumel.* 1: 387 (1843)

Leaves 3–4 per bulb, 0.7–1.2 cm wide, with scabrid margins. Raceme rather lax, cylindrical. Pedicels 6–12 mm long at flowering time. Flowers 4–6 mm long, the upper sterile ones violet, the lower fertile ones brownish-purple, the lobes about as long as the tube. Areas 2, 9, 11 (endemic).

B. crassa Wendelbo in *Notes Roy. Bot. Gard. Edinb.* 38, 3: 424 (1980)

This was described in the fruiting state. Leaves two per bulb, obovate, 2.6–3.3 cm wide, rather short and broad. The raceme is very dense, with large fleshy capsules only just raised above the ground. The remains of the flowers suggest a pale colour; they are about 5 mm long. Scree slopes. Area 4 (known only from Refahiye).

B. dubia (Guss.) Roemer & Schultes subsp. *boissieri* (Freyn) Feinbr. in *Palest. Jour. Bot. Jerusalem* Ser. 1, 2: 348 (1939)

Leaves two to five, with glabrous margins, about 0.5–1 cm wide. Raceme cylindrical. Pedicels about 5 mm long. Flowers 5–7 mm long, blue in bud becoming violet or greenish, the lobes about one third as long as the tube. Area 6 (and in the Balkans).

B. fomini Woronow in *Bull. Jard. Bot. Princ.* 26: 617 (1927)

Leaves three to five, with smooth or rough margins, 1–2 cm wide. Raceme cylindrical. Pedicels 5–7 mm long. Flowers 6–7 mm long, violet in bud, greyish-lilac when open, with blackish lobes about half as long as the tube. Areas 17, 18 (and in Transcaucasia). No other species has blackish lobes.

B. forniculata (Fomin) Deloney in *Monit. Jard. Bot. Tiflis* 1: 44 (1922–23). (Syn. *Muscari forniculatum* Fomin)

This is a dwarf species with bright blue flowers in a short dense raceme, looking rather *Muscari*-like; the flower however is typical of *Bellevalia* and is not constricted at the mouth. Wet alpine meadows. Areas ?4, 14 (and in USSR).

This is the only species to have bright blue flowers; *B. paradoxa* and *B. pycnantha* (see below) have dark, rather dull blue coloration.

B. gracilis Feinbr. in *Palest. Jour. Bot. Jerusalem Ser.* 1, 2: 363 (1939)

Leaves two to three, with ciliate margins, 2.7–3.2 cm wide. Raceme conical, fairly dense. Pedicels about 1–2 cm long, very slender at the flowering stage, up to 5 cm long in fruit. Flowers 6–7.5 mm long, yellow or whitish in bud, dirty brown when open, the lobes about half as long as the tube. Areas 3, 8, 12, 13 (endemic). A rather compact plant with noticeably thin pedicels.

The Turkish specimen cited by Feinbrun as *B. albana* Woronow is in fact *B. gracilis*; *B. albana* does not occur in Turkey.

B. kurdistanica Feinbr. in *Palest. Jour. Bot. Jerusalem Ser.* 1, 2: 381 (1939)

Leaves five to six, with ciliate margins, 1.7–2 cm wide. Raceme dense, many-flowered, cylindrical in the later stages. Pedicels 5–7 mm long at flowering time. Flowers 8–10 mm long, pale lilac at first, changing to whitish, the lobes much shorter than the tube. Area 16 (and N. Iraq).

B. latifolia Feinbr. in *Palest. Jour. Bot. Jerusalem Ser.* 1, 2: 369 (1939)

Leaves five to seven, densely ciliate on the margins, usually 4–8 cm wide. Raceme ovate or conical, many-flowered. Pedicels 2–3 cm long, elongating in fruit to 5–6 cm. Flowers 1–1.3 cm long, green in bud, becoming white with green veins and later brownish, the lobes about one third as long as the tube. Area 16 (and N. Iraq).

B. longistyla (Miscz.) Grossh., *Fl. Kavk.* 1: 234 (1928)

Leaves 3–5, rather short and broad, with ciliate margins, 2–3 cm wide. Raceme short, rather loose, cylindrical or ellipsoid. Pedicels 1–1.5 cm long, elongating up to 8 cm in the fruiting stage. Flowers 1–1.2 cm long, dull purple in bud, becoming brownish or dirty white, the lobes about one third to half as long as the tube. Areas 13, 15 (and in Iran and Caucasus).

This is a rather stocky plant at first but expanding enormously in the fruiting stage, with the leaves reaching 6 cm in width.

B. modesta Wendelbo in *Notes Roy. Bot. Gard. Edinb.* 38, 3: 425 (1980)

Leaves three to five, with ciliate margins, up to 2 cm wide. Raceme cylindrical, many-flowered but rather loose. Pedicels 4–6 mm long at flowering time. Flowers 5–8 mm long, creamy-coloured, shaded purplish-brown, with lobes equal in length to the tube. Area 8 (endemic).

B. paradoxa (Fischer & C. Meyer) Boiss., *Fl. Or.* 5: 308 (1884). (Syn. *Muscari paradoxum* (Fischer & C. Meyer) K. Koch)

This is similar to *B. forniculata* (see above) in having blue flowers in a short, dense, almost capitate, raceme but they are of a much darker blackish-blue. Wet mountain meadows. Areas ?4, 14 (and in Transcaucasia).

B. pycnantha (K. Koch) Los.-Losinsk. in Fl. URSS 4: 404 (1935). (Syn. Muscari pycnanthum K. Koch)

A robust plant to 30 cm in height. Flowers deep dull blue or blackish-blue with yellowish margins to the lobes, produced on short pedicels in a dense conical raceme. Wet meadows. Areas 14, 15, 16 (and in N. Iraq and Iran).

B. rixii Wendelbo in Notes Roy. Bot. Gard. Edinb. 38, 3: 431 (1980)

Leaves two, rather falcate. A dwarf plant with deep violet-blue flowers in a short dense raceme, rather like B. paradoxa, but it differs in having very short pedicels, only 0.5–1.5 mm long, in its channelled and arched leaves (flat and erect in B. paradoxa) and in having violet anthers (yellow in B. paradoxa). Areas 15, 16 (endemic).

B. sarmatica (Pallas) Woronow in Bull. Jard. Bot. Princ. 26: 615 (1927). (Syn. B. trojana Feinbr., B. ciliata (Cirillo) Nees)

Leaves three to seven, with ciliate margins, 1.2–2.7 cm wide. Raceme conical. Pedicels 1.5–2.5 cm long at flowering time, elongating later. Flowers 8–11 mm long, purplish, fading to brownish-purple, the lobes one third as long as the tube. Areas 1, 5, 6, 8, 9, 10, 11, 12, 13, 14, 15 (and in other E. Mediterranean countries).

B. tauri Feinbr. in Palest. Jour Bot. Jerusalem Ser. 1, 2: 352 (1939)

Leaves four, with glabrous or scabrid margins, about 1 cm wide. Raceme cylindrical. Pedicels 6–7 mm long. Flowers 6–7 mm long, probably brownish-purple. Area 8 (endemic). A rather poorly known species from the Cilician Taurus.

B. trifoliata (Ten.) Kunth, Enum. Pl. 4:308 (1843)

Leaves two to four, glabrous or ciliate on the margins, 1.2–3 cm wide. Raceme cylindrical. Pedicels 5–8 mm long at flowering time. Flowers 1–1.6 cm long, deep violet in bud turning brownish-purple, the lobes about a half to a quarter the length of the tube. Areas 1, 6, 7, 8 (and widespread in the E. Mediterranean).

B. warburgii (Pallas) Woronow. A species from Syria and Israel, has been cited as occurring in S.E. Turkey but this is probably based on a misidentification.

3 Chionodoxa (English: Glory of the Snow; Turkish: Karyıldızı)

A small genus, related to Scilla and easily distinguished from it by the perianth segments being joined into a short tube at the base and by the stamens, which have broad flattened filaments held together so that they look like a cone in the centre of the flower. They have two basal leaves and racemes of blue flowers.

Crocus asumaniae near Akseki, Antalya.

22 *Crocus cancellatus* corms on sale in Gaziantep.

Crocus karduchorum near Hizan, Bitlis.

24 *Crocus kotschyanus* subsp. *cappadocicus* between Darende and Pınarbaşı, Sivas.

25 *Crocus kotschyanus* subsp. *suworowianus* between Ikizdere and Ispir, Erzurum.

26 *Crocus pallasii* subsp. *turcicus* at Urfa.

27 *Crocus pulchellus* on Ulu Dağ, Bursa.

28 *Crocus sativus*. A Saffron-gatherer at Safranbolu, Zonguldak.

29 *Crocus scharojanii* on Zigana Dağ, Trabzon.

30 *Crocus vallicola* on Zigana Dağ, Trabzon.

31 *Gladiolus communis* near Istanbul.

32 *Gladiolus kotschyanus* at Şemdinli, Hakkâri.

33 *Gynandriris sisyrinchium* at Bornova, Izmir.

34 *Iris attica* near Bilecik.

35 *Iris purpureobractea* from Honaz Dağ, Denizli.

36 *Iris schachtii* near Beynam, Ankara.

37 *Iris suaveolens* between Çankırı and Çerkeş.

38 *Iris taochia* near Tortum, Erzurum.

39 *Iris barnumae* at Van.

40 *Iris gatesii* on Halkis Dăg, Sason, Siirt.

1 *Iris iberica* subsp. *elegantissima* near Oltu, Erzurum.

42 *Iris paradoxa* forma *choschab* on the Çuğ Pass, Van.

44 *Iris lazica* near Rize.

43 *Iris sari* at Şereflikoçhisar, Ankara.

45 *Iris masia* at Siverek, Urfa.

46 *Iris sintenisii* at Lake Abant, Bolu.

47 *Iris spuria* subsp. *musulmanica* at Hakkâri.

48 *Iris xanthospuria* at Köyceğiz, Muğla.

49 *Iris bakeriana* between Mardin and Savur.

50 *Iris histrio* near Silifke at Uzuncaburç, Mersin.

51 *Iris histrioides* from Ak Dağ, Amasya.

52 *Iris pamphylica* near Akseki, Antalya.

53 *Iris reticulata* on Palandöken Dağ, Erzurum.

54 *Iris aucheri* between Diyarbakır and Ergani.

55 *Iris caucasica* subsp. *turcicus* at Yozgat.

56 *Iris galatica* at Lake Hazar, Elaziğ.

57 *Iris persica* from west of Gaziantep.

58 *Romulea linaresii* near Istanbul.

59 *Allium akaka* near Horasan, Erzurum.

60 *Bellevalia longistyla* in eastern Turkey.

5 H. J. Elwes 1846–1922

6 E. Forbes 1815–1854

7 H. K. Haussknecht 1838–1903

8 *Above right* K. Koch 1809–1879

9 Th. Kotschy 1813–1866

In Turkey there are about three or four species; the only ones to occur outside Turkey are in Crete (two species) and in Cyprus (one species). They are not very common plants, occurring mainly on the mountains of W. Turkey near melting snow. There is a mystery concerning one of the species and it seems likely that the original information given about the type locality is incorrect. They all flower in early spring, March to May.

All the Turkish species of *Chionodoxa* are valuable spring-flowering bulbs for the rock garden or for naturalizing in semi-shade. Particularly easy and prolific is the plant sold as *C. luciliae* which produces its bluish, white-eyed flowers with great freedom. In cultivation there are white and pink forms also.

C. forbesii Baker in *Journ. Linn. Soc.* 11: 436 (1871)

This has several rich blue flowers in a loose raceme, each flower about 2 cm diameter.

For more than a century this species remained a mystery, known only from the rather poor dried specimens collected by Forbes. Now it has been re-collected by S. V. Horton and by O. Sønderhousen in the Mountains north-east of Fethiye. It is very similar to the '*C. luciliae* of gardens' (see under *C. luciliae* below) and may well prove to be the correct name for it. Area 7 (endemic).

C. gigantea Whittall in Barr & Son, *Autumn Catalogue* 1889: 3 (1889)

The most distinctive species, with large, 3 cm diameter, lilac-blue, usually erect flowers, only one to three in a lax raceme. Mountain turf and in rocks. Area 6 (endemic, known from Boz Dağ, Ödemis). This should now be called *C. luciliae* Boiss. (see below).

C. luciliae Boiss., *Diagn. Pl. Or. Nov.* Ser. 1, 5: 61 (1844)

The original *C. luciliae* of Boissier is the same as *C. gigantea* and is the older and therefore correct name for it, but in cultivation '*C. luciliae*' is applied to a plant with smaller, 2–2.5 cm diameter, blue flowers which are carried in a many-flowered one-sided raceme. The name of this latter well-known plant has yet to be clarified but it is probably the same as *C. forbesii* Baker. '*C. luciliae*' occurs in area 6 (endemic, known from Nif Dağ, Izmir).

C. sardensis Barr & Sugden, *Catalogue* (1883)

This is easily recognized by virtue of its several intensely deep blue flowers with a small white eye. They are produced in a loose raceme. Alpine turf. Area 6 (endemic).

C. siehei Stapf in *Bot. Mag.* t. 9068 (1925)

This is said to have originated from Ala Dağ in the Anti-Taurus but has not been re-collected there. It is a very robust plant with many rich purple-blue flowers which have a large white eye. It is very similar to '*C. luciliae* of the gardens' and may only be a good form of it. It was described from material grown in Glasnevin Botanic Garden and not directly from a wild collection.

C. tmoli Whittall

This is an unpublished name referring to material sent out by Whittall from Boz Dağ (Tmolus) and seems to have been a form of *C. luciliae* Boiss. (*C. gigantea*). In cultivation today the plant grown as *C. tmoli* is applied to a form of '*C. luciliae* of gardens'.

4 *Colchicum* (English: Meadow Saffron; Turkish: Aciçiğdem)

Short, stemless plants with tunicated corms, the tunics membranous, brown or blackish. Leaves produced with the flowers (most spring-flowering species) or after the flowers (most autumn-flowering species), linear to broadly elliptic. Flowers white, lilac or purple, erect and wine-glass shaped with six perianth segments joined into a long tube. Stamens six, inserted at the throat. Ovary subterranean until maturity when it is pushed up with the expanding leaves to well above the surface. Styles three, long and thread-like with terminal or lateral stigmas near the apex. Fruit a many-seeded capsule. Seeds globose, brown, usually large.

An Old World genus of about 40 species mainly distributed in the Mediterranean region but extending to northern Europe (one species) and east to Iran, Afghanistan and the western Himalayas. In Turkey there are about 25 species.

Most *Colchicum* species are of horticultural value, especially the large-flowered autumnal ones. Some species are very common in the wild and, since they are poisonous to livestock, are disliked by farmers. The bulbs and seeds have medicinal value and the substance Colchicine is prepared from them.

The Turkish species are divided here into two groups, and are arranged alphabetically within the groups. The first are those which are *Spring-flowering* (leaves present at flowering time); the second are the *Autumn-flowering* (leaves usually produced after the flowers).

In addition to the species known to occur in Turkey the following have also been mentioned in literature:

C. autumnale L., a European species, has been recorded in Area 5 but its presence requires confirmation. *C. haussknechtii* Boiss., from Iran, has been recorded from E. Turkey but this may be a case of mistaken identity (but see *Colchicum sp.*, page 75). The Caucasian species *C. laetum* Steven has been attributed to N.E. Turkey but no authentic material has been seen. *C. obtusifolium* (Siehe) Hayek is a name in need of further investigation; it is possibly based on a mixture of two other species. *C. byzantinum* Parkinson has long been in cultivation but its origin is unknown; it may be a hybrid of garden origin.

For garden display purposes it is mainly the showy autumn-flowering species which are cultivated since the spring ones are, on the whole, small and not so easy to grow. The robust ones such as *C. speciosum*, *C. bivonae* and *C. cilicicum* will grow well in well-drained sunny positions and are very hardy.

Spring-flowering (leaves partly developed)

C. burttii Meikle in *Bot. Mag.* N.S. 181, t. 735 (1977)

This is very similar to *C. triphyllum* (see below) but differs in having rather tough blackish corm tunics, distinctly hairy margins to the three leaves and brownish stamens in which the filaments are conspicuously hairy at the base. The slender flowers are white or pale pink. Rocky places at low altitudes, to 1,500 metres. Areas 1, 5, 6, 7 (and in the E. Aegean Is.).

C. falcifolium Stapf in *Denkschr. Akad. Wiss. Math.-Nat. Kl. Wien* 50, 1: 19 (1885). (Syn. *C. hiemale* Siehe, *C. hirsutum* Stefanoff, ?*C. lockmanni* Siehe, *C. serpentinum* Woronow ex Miscz., *C. tauri* Siehe ex Stefanoff, *C. varians* Freyn & Bornm. ex Freyn).

Flowers usually two to six, white, pink or purplish, 1.5–2.5 cm diameter, often with very narrow segments giving the flower a starry appearance; anthers brownish or blackish. Leaves three to five, glabrous or whitish-hairy, narrow, usually 5 mm or less wide, about 2–5 cm long at flowering time. Dry rocky places in the mountains, flowering as the snow melts, to 1,600 metres. Areas 3, 4, 8, 11, 12, 13, 17, 18 (and in Syria and Iran).

C. szovitsii Fischer & C. Meyer in *Ind. Sem. Hort. Petrop.* 1: 24 (1834). (Syn. *C. acutifolium* Siehe, *C. armenum* B. Fedtsch., *C. bifolium* Freyn & Sint., *C. hydrophilum* Siehe, *C. hygrophilum* Siehe, *C. nivale* Boiss. & Huet, *C. syriacum* Siehe)

Flowers one to six, pink, purplish or white, often with broad overlapping segments giving the flower a globular appearance, 1.5–2.5 cm in diameter; anthers usually dark purple before releasing the yellow pollen. Leaves glabrous, normally two but rarely three, short at flowering time, at most reaching to the base of the flower, usually rather broad, 5–30 mm depending on stage of development. Damp alpine turf near melting snow, to about 3,000 metres. Areas 1, 2, 4, 5, 6, 7, 8, 9, 10, 11, 12, 13, 14, 15, 16, 18 (and in Iran and Caucasus).

C. triphyllum Kunze in *Flora* 29: 755 (1846) (Syn. *C. ancyrense* B. L. Burtt)

Flowers one to three, pinkish, purplish or nearly white with a yellow centre; about 1.5–2.5 cm diameter; anthers brownish-black or purplish-black with yellow pollen. Leaves three usually glabrous, short at flowering time and about 5–10 mm wide. Corm tunics very thin, papery, brown. Open stony places in the mountains, to 2,000 metres. Areas ?2, 3, 6, 7, 8, 9, 10, 11, 12, ?13 (and widespread in the Mediterranean region).

Autumn-flowering

The leaves of these are usually absent (but see *C. stevenii, C. psaridis and C. baytopiorum*).

C. balansae Planchon in *Ann. Sci. Nat.* Sér. 4, 4: 145 (1855). (Syn. *C. candidum* Schott & Kotschy)

Flowers several, about 5 cm diameter with segments 4–7 cm long, rosy-pink, or rarely white, not tessellated; anthers yellow. Leaves absent at flowering time, shiny green, up to 30 cm long and 7 cm wide at maturity. A peculiarity of this species is the extreme depth at which the corms occur, as much as 50 cm, with a long blackish-brown neck of tunics. Open rocky places and in rocky scrub, to 1,900 metres. Areas 7, 8 (and in Rhodes).

C. baytopiorum C. Brickell in Notes Roy. Bot. Gard. Edinb. 41, 1: 49 (1983)

Flowers usually one to three, about 4–6 cm in diameter with segments 2.5–4 cm long, pinkish-purple, not tessellated; anthers yellow, filaments with a swollen yellow base. Leaves three, bright shiny green, usually up to 5 cm long, but sometimes only very shortly developed, at flowering time expanding later to about 15 cm long. Rocky places in woodland. Area 7 (endemic).

C. bivonae Guss. in Cat. Pl. Boccad.: 5 (1821) (Syn. C. bowlesianum B. L. Burtt, C. latifolium Sibth. & Smith, C. sibthorpii hort.)

Flowers several, very large, 4.5–6.5 cm diameter with segments 6–8 cm long, deep rosy-purple, strongly tessellated; anthers purplish. Leaves absent at flowering time, later developing up to 35 cm long and 3–5 cm broad. Open rocky places and in light woodland, to 1,400 metres. Areas 1, 2, 5 (and in Aegean Is., Balkans, S. Italy, Corsica and Sardinia).

C. boissieri Orph. in Atti Congr. Int. Bot. Firenze 1874: 31 (1876). (Syn. C. procurrens Baker)

Corm creeping horizontally in a stolon-like manner. Flowers usually solitary, but sometimes two or three, about 3–4 cm diameter, bright pinkish-purple, not tessellated; anthers yellow. Leaves absent at flowering time, usually two to three, dark green, erect, rather narrow with a blunt apex, up to 20 cm long. Open stony or grassy places on limestone to 1,500 metres. Areas 5, 6, 7 (and in S. Greece).

C. bornmuelleri Freyn in Ber. Deutsch. Bot. Ges. 7: 319 (1889)

This is very similar in general appearance to *C. speciosum* (see below) but has purplish, not yellow, anthers. Areas 2, 3, 6, 9, 10. Alpine meadows and woods, to 2,000 metres (endemic).

C. chalcedonicum Azn. in Bull. Soc. Bot. Fr. 44: 174 (1897)

Flowers usually solitary, 2–3 cm diameter with segments 6–8 cm long, deep rosy-purple, distinctly tessellated; anthers yellow or brownish. Leaves appearing after the flowers, five to nine, grey-green, about 1 cm wide. Stony places to 3,000 metres. Areas 1, 5 (endemic).

C. cilicicum Dammer in Gard. Chron. 23: 34 (1898)

Flowers one to several, large, 4–6 cm diameter with segments 4.5–7 cm long, pale to deep pinkish-lilac, usually not tessellated; anthers yellow. Leaves appearing after the flowers, about five, 5–10 cm wide. Rocky slopes, often in light woodland, to 2,000 metres. Areas 7, 8 (endemic).

C. kotschyi Boiss., *Diagn. Pl. Or. Nov.* Ser. 1, 13: 38 (1853) (Syn. *C. imperatoris-friderici* Siehe)

Flowers up to ten, about 3–4 cm diameter, slender with narrow segments about 3.5–5 cm long, white or pale pink, not (or very rarely) tessellated; anthers yellow. Leaves appearing after the flowers, three to four per corm, about 2–4 cm wide, rather blunt at the apex. Hillsides and fields in the mountains, often in oak scrub, to 3,000 metres. Areas 6, 7, 8, 10, 13, 15, 18 (and in N. Iraq, Iran).

C. lingulatum Boiss. & Spruner, *Diagn. Pl. Or. Nov.* Ser. 1, 5: 66 (1844)

Flowers one to four, about 3–4 cm diameter with narrow non-overlapping segments up to 5 cm long, pale pink, not tessellated; anthers yellow. Leaves appearing after the flowers, three to five, glaucous and often lying flat on the ground, 1–2 cm wide, blunt at the apex. Open stony places and in scrub, to 1,000 metres. Area 6 (and in Rhodes and Greece).

C. micranthum Boiss., *Fl. Or.* 5: 162 (1884)

Flowers small, one to two, about 1–2 cm diameter with segments 1.5–2.5 cm long, pale pink, not tessellated; anthers yellow. Leaves appearing after the flowers, two to three, shiny green, only 0.5–1 cm wide. Meadows, at low altitudes. Areas 1, 5 (endemic).

C. macrophyllum B. L. Burtt in *Kew Bull.* 1950: 433 (1951)

Flowers one to two, rather large, flattish when fully open, about 5–7 cm diameter with broad segments overlapping at the base, pale pink, distinctly tessellated; anthers pinkish-purple. Leaves shiny green, appearing after the flowers, very broad, up to 15 cm wide, and strongly pleated. Stony and rocky banks, often in woods, at low altitudes. Area 6 (and in Rhodes and Crete).

C. psaridis Heldr. ex Hal., *Consp. Fl. Graec.* 3: 274 (1904)

Flowers one to four, small, 1–2 cm diameter with narrow segments, pale pinkish-purple, not tessellated; anthers blackish or purplish. Leaves two to three, present at flowering time, only 5–15 mm wide. Corm creeping horizontally, stolon-like. Stony hills, to 1850 m. Area 7 (and in S. Greece).

C. sieheanum Hausskn. ex Stefanoff in *Sborn. Bălg. Akad. Nauk* 22: 47 (1926)

A poorly known species requiring further study. If it is the same plant as was collected by T. Baytop in autumn 1983 at Fındıkpınar in the Taurus Mts (i.e. the type locality of *C. sieheanum*) it has the following characteristics. Flowers one to two, bright purplish-pink, darker towards the tips of the segments and almost white in the throat, not tessellated, 2.5–3.5 cm diameter with segments about 2.5–4 cm long; anthers yellow. Leaves appearing after the flowers. Corm erect, but with a slight tendency to the stolon-like behaviour of *C. boissieri*. Rocky slopes. Area 8 (endemic).

C. D. Brickell in *Notes Roy. Bot. Gard. Edinb.* 41, 1: 51 (1983) discusses this species at some length; he considers that it is possibly the same as *C. boissieri*, but more data is needed to be sure.

C. speciosum Steven in *Nouv. Mém. Soc. Nat. Moscou* 7: 265 (1829)

Flowers one to three, about 4–7 cm diameter with broad overlapping segments up to 8 cm long, pinkish-purple to reddish-purple, sometimes with a large white throat, normally not tessellated; tube white, greenish or purplish; anthers yellow. Leaves appearing after the flowers, shiny green, four to six, lanceolate or elliptical, up to 10 cm wide. Meadows or light woodland. Areas 3, 4, ?8 (and in N. Iran, Caucasus).

C. stevenii Kunth, *Enum. Pl.* 4: 144 (1841) (Syn. *C. polyphyllum* Boiss. & Heldr.)

An autumn-flowering species but with the leaves well-developed at flowering time. Flowers usually one to five, rather small and starry, about 1.5–2.5 cm diameter with narrow non-overlapping segments 2–3 cm long, deep pink, not tessellated; anthers yellow. Leaves about four to seven, narrowly linear, only 2–4 mm wide, usually about as long as the flower at the flowering stage. Dry rocky places to 1,500 metres. Areas 6, 7, 8 (and in Syria, Lebanon, Israel, Cyprus).

C. troodii Kotschy, *Die Insel Cyp.*:180 (1862). (Syn. *C. decaisnei* Boiss.)

Flowers starry, about four to six per corm, pale pink or white, 2.5–3 cm diameter with narrow segments about 3–4 cm long; anthers yellow. Leaves appearing after the flowers, three to seven, about 1–3 cm wide. Dry rocky places to 1,500 metres. Areas 7, 8, ?13, ?17 (and in Cyprus, Syria, Israel, Lebanon).

C. turcicum Janka in *Österr. Bot. Zeitschr.* 23: 242 (1873)

Flowers usually two to three, sometimes more, 1.5–3 cm diameter with narrow segments 3–4 cm long, pale to deep magenta, not tessellated or faintly so; anthers yellow or possibly brownish. Leaves appearing after the flowers, narrowly lanceolate, 1–2 cm wide, greyish green, sometimes twisted lengthways. Open fields and stony places at low altitudes. Areas 1, 5 (and in E. Bulgaria, S. Jugoslavia, N. Greece, ?E. Roumania).

C. umbrosum Steven in *Nouv. Mém. Soc. Nat. Moscou* 7: 264 (1829). (Syn. *C. trapezuntinum* Boiss.)

Flowers one to five, small, usually 1–1.5 cm diameter, with the segments 1.5–2.5 cm long, often unequal and curved inwards at the apex, pale pink or whitish, not tessellated; anthers yellow. Leaves appearing after the flowers, three to five, lanceolate, about 1–2 cm wide, shiny green. Light woodland or scrub, to 1,500 metres. Areas 2, 3, 4, 5 (and in Crimea and Caucasus).

C. variegatum L., *Sp. Pl.*: 342 (1753)

Flowers flattish, 5–10 cm in diameter with broad segments up to 6 cm long, overlapping at the base and acute at the apex, pinkish-carmine, strongly tessellated; anthers purple-pink. Leaves appearing after the flowers, three to four, lanceolate, usually undulate at the margins, often grey-green, about 1–2 cm wide. Stony places in scrub or light woodland, to 1,500 metres. Areas 6, 7, 8 (and in Aegean Is. and Cyclades).

C. sp.

In Areas 8, 17 and 18, in dry regions near Gaziantep and Urfa, there is an autumn-flowering species with plain or slightly tessellated pinkish-lilac flowers about 2–4 cm in diameter. It is leafless at flowering time; the leaves follow in spring and are numerous (up to 20) and only 4–10 mm wide. We have not yet identified this satisfactorily and it may represent an undescribed species or possibly be a variant of *C. haussknechtii* Boiss. or of *C. hierosolymitanum* Feinbrun.

5 *Fritillaria* (English: Fritillary, Snake's Head Lily; Turkish: Terslâle)

Well-known lily-like plants with pendulous bell-shaped flowers often in dull brownish, greenish or purplish colours and sometimes chequered or tessellated.

Short to tall bulbous plants, the bulbs usually with two thick scales not enclosed in a tunic. Stems with alternate, opposite or sometimes whorled leaves which are linear or lanceolate. Flowers nodding, bell-shaped or conical. Perianth segments six, with glistening nectaries which vary from small and more or less ovate or circular to narrowly linear or lanceolate. Stamens six, inserted at the base of the segments. Style entire to trifid. Fruit a dry capsule with three rounded or winged valves. Seeds numerous, flat.

A genus of about 75 species distributed through the temperate Northern Hemisphere. In Turkey there are about 30 species. All are spring-flowering, usually March to May, depending upon altitude.

The many and varied species of fritillary are popular with bulb specialists although a lot of them have flowers in rather subdued colours. In cultivation they mostly require sun and well-drained soils and in climates with a damp summer must be given protection during their dormant period.

F. acmopetala Boiss., Diagn. Pl. Or. Nov. Ser. 1, 7: 104 (1846). (Syn. F. lycia Boiss. & Heldr.)

About 30–45 cm in height. Leaves grey-green, narrowly linear or linear-lanceolate, alternate. Flowers 3–4 cm wide, usually solitary, broadly campanulate, green with brown tips or with a brown band on each of the segments, sometimes the inner segments almost wholly brown; tips of the segments curved outwards. Style deeply three-lobed. Fields and stony places. Areas 6, 7, 8 (and in Syria, Lebanon and Cyprus).

Subsp. *wendelboi* Rix has fewer, broader (up to 3 cm) leaves and rather squarer bells. Areas 7, 8, 10 (endemic).

F. alburyana Rix in Notes from Roy. Bot. Gard. Edinb. 31, 1: 128 (1971) (Syn: F. erzurumica Kasapligil)

Usually less than 10 cm tall. Leaves alternate, grey-green. Flowers solitary, very widely campanulate, pink with darker veining, up to 5·5 cm diameter. Style slender, glabrous, shortly three-lobed at the apex. Stony mountainsides and in alpine turf. Areas 4, 13, 14, 15 (endemic).

F. alfredae Post in *Mém. Herb. Boiss*. 18: 101 (1900) subsp. *alfredae*

This occurs only in Lebanon but in Turkey there are two further subspecies of *F. alfredae*:

F. alfredae subsp. *platyptera* (Samuelsson) Rix in *Kew Bull*. 33, 4: 596 (1979). 15–30 cm tall. Leaves narrowly linear, alternate or subopposite, the upper in a whorl of three, green. Flowers one to two, very narrowly campanulate, grey-green on the exterior, yellow-green inside, about 1–1.5 cm diameter. Style thick, papillose, more or less entire or slightly three-lobed at the apex. In oak scrub. Area 8 (and in N. Syria).

F. alfredae subsp. *glaucoviridis* (Turrill) Rix in *Kew Bull*. 33: 598 (1979). (Syn. *F. glaucoviridis* Turrill, *F. haradjianii* Briq. ex Rech. fil.) Similar to subsp. *platyptera* but generally with more leaves on the stem (usually nine to ten), the lowest of which are oblanceolate or ovate, whereas in subsp. *platyptera* they are usually about seven in number, the lowest are linear-lanceolate and the upper are longer than those of a subsp. *glaucoviridis*. Oak and beech woods, or in scrub. Area 8 (endemic).

F. armena Boiss., *Diagn. Pl. Or. Nov*. Ser. 1, 7: 106 (1846)

Plant 5–20 cm in height. Leaves alternate, grey-green. Flowers usually solitary, narrowly campanulate, deep purplish-brown or dark red-wine colour inside and out, to 1.5 cm diameter. Style rather thick, papillose, entire or shortly three-lobed. Alpine meadows and stony slopes. Areas 12, 13, 14, 15, (endemic).

F. assyriaca Baker in *Jour. Linn. Soc*. 14: 265 (1874) (Syn. *F. canaliculata* Baker)

Plant 10–25 cm in height. Leaves narrowly lanceolate, grey-green, channel-led, alternate but carried mainly on the upper part of the stem. Flowers usually solitary, narrowly campanulate, the colour very variable from dull violet with a greyish 'bloom' on the exterior, and with yellow margins and tips to the segments, to greenish, or bicoloured green and violet, up to 1.5 cm diameter. Style thick, entire. In fields or on hillsides. Areas 13, 14, 15, 18 (and in W. Iran).

Subsp. *melananthera* Rix has flowers which are green and blackish inside, with blackish anthers (yellowish inside, with yellow anthers, in subsp. *assyriaca*). Area 8 (endemic).

F. aurea Schott in *Österr. Bot. Wochenblatt*. 4: 137 (1854) (Syn: *F. cilicico-taurica* Hausskn. & Bornm.)

Plant 5–15 cm in height. Leaves alternate, or the two basal ones subopposite, grey-green. Flowers usually solitary, broadly campanulate, yellow with a network of red-brown veining, up to 3.5 cm diameter. Style slender, three-lobed at the apex. Alpine turf or rocky slopes. Areas 8, 11, 12, 13 (endemic). This is very similar to the chocolate-brown-flowered *F. nobilis* (see under *F. latifolia*).

F. bithynica Baker in *Jour. Linn. Soc*. 14: 264 (1874) (Syn: *F. dasyphylla* Baker; *F. schliemannii* Sint.; *F. citrina* Baker; *F. pineticola* O. Schwarz)

Usually 10–20 cm in height. Leaves green or slightly grey-green, the lowest pair opposite, the rest alternate, or the upper three whorled. Flowers one to two, narrowly campanulate, green, greenish-yellow or bicoloured green and pale brownish-purple, sometimes glaucous, up to 1.5 cm diameter. Style glabrous, slender. In scrub or pine forest. Areas 5, 6, 7 (and in E. Aegean Is.).

F. carica Rix in *Kew Bull.* 30, 1:156 (1975)

About 5–15 cm tall. Leaves usually alternate, grey-green. Flowers one to three, narrowly campanulate, yellow or greenish-yellow, up to 2 cm diameter. Style papillose, thick, entire or slightly three-lobed at the apex. Rocky places, often in sparse pine woods. Areas 6, 7 (and in E. Aegean Is.).

Subsp. *serpenticola* Rix has fewer, broadly lanceolate leaves and conical flowers with a slender style. Area 7 (endemic).

F. caucasica Adams in Weber & Mohr, *Beitr. Naturk.* 1: 51 (1805)

About 10–30 cm in height. Leaves alternate, slightly greyish-green. Flowers one to two, campanulate, rather larger and wider than those of the similar *F. armena*, dark purplish-brown with a glaucous exterior, about 1.5–2.5 cm wide at the mouth. Style slender, undivided. Alpine meadows and sparse conifer woods. Areas 3, 4, 13, 14, 15 (and in N.W. Iran, Caucasus).

F. crassifolia Boiss. & Huet in Boiss., *Diagn. Pl. Or. Nov.* Ser. 2, 4: 103 (1859)

In Turkey there are three subspecies:

F. crassifolia subsp. *crassifolia* (Syn. *F. ophioglossifolia* Freyn & Sint.) About 5–10 cm tall. Leaves alternate, grey-green. Flowers one to two, broadly campanulate, dull yellow or greenish, tessellated with brown or purple, 2–3 cm in diameter. Style three-lobed. Stony places. Areas 4, 6, 7, 8, 10, 13, 14 (endemic).

F. crassifolia subsp. *kurdica* (Boiss. & Noë) Rix in *Kew Bull.* 29, 4: 638 (1974) (Syn: *F. kurdica* Boiss. & Nöe, *F. wanensis* Freyn, *F. karadaghensis* Turrill, *F. grossheimiana* Los.-Losinsk., *F. foliosa* Bornm.) Similar to the above but has five to six narrow leaves (subsp. *crassifolia* usually has four). Subsp. *kurdica* differs also in having some raised ridges on the inside of the perianth segments. The flowers are very variable in colour, usually tessellated brown on a green ground, sometimes very strongly, so as to appear almost wholly brown. Stony places or in alpine scrub. Areas 13, 15, 16 (and in S. Russia, N. Iraq, N.W. Iran).

F. crassifolia subsp. *hakkarensis* Rix in *Kew Bull.* 29, 4: 641 (1974). Similar to subsp. *kurdica* but has shiny green leaves and the perianth segments are acute (obtuse in subsp. *kurdica*). Stony places near melting snow. Area 16 (and in N.E. Iraq).

F. elwesii Boiss., *Fl. Or.* 5: 181 (1884) (Syn: *F. sieheana* Hausskn.)

A tall slender plant about 20–35 cm in height. Leaves alternate, very narrow, grey-green. Flowers usually solitary, narrowly campanulate, brownish-purple with a broad green band along the outer segments, not tessellated, up to 1.5 cm diameter. Style three-lobed at the apex. Sparse pine woods or scrub. Areas 7, 8 (endemic).

F. fleischeriana Steudel & Hochst. ex Schultes, *Syst. Veg.* 7: 388 (1829)

About 5–15 cm in height. Leaves grey-green, linear, the lowest opposite, the rest alternate. Flowers narrowly campanulate, up to three, purple-brown with a green stripe along the centre of each segment. Style more or less entire. Stony places. Areas 6, 9 (endemic).

F. forbesii Baker in *Jour. Linn. Soc.* 14: 264 (1874)

About 10–20 cm in height. Leaves usually all alternate, very narrowly linear-lanceolate, grey-green. Flowers solitary, narrowly campanulate with the segments curved outwards at the tips, greenish-yellow, up to 1.5 cm diameter. Style entire or shortly three-lobed. Scrub and sparse *Pinus brutia* woods. Areas 6, 7 (endemic).

F. hermonis Fenzl in Kotschy, *Pl. Syr. Exsicc.* 1855

In Turkey this species is represented by subsp. *amana*; subsp. *hermonis* occurs only in Lebanon.

 F. hermonis subsp. *amana* Rix in *Kew Bull.* 29, 4: 647 (1974). About 10–35 cm in height. Leaves alternate, bright green. Flowers are to three, broadly campanulate, green tessellated with brown to a varying degree so as to appear either greenish or brownish, 2.5–3.5 cm diameter. Style distinctly three-lobed. Mountain slopes. Area 8 (and in Syria and Lebanon). This is superficially similar to *F. crassifolia* but the shape of the nectary is different. In *F. crassifolia* it is long and linear while in *F. hermonis* it is shorter and lanceolate or ovate.

F. imperialis L., *Sp. Pl.*: 303 (1753) (Syn: *F. aintabensis* Post) (Turkish name: Şahtuğu)

About 50–100 cm in height. Leaves bright green, in whorls, usually on the upper half of the stems. Flowers large, one to five in a whorl, broadly campanulate, orange, up to 5 cm diameter. Style three-lobed. In scrub and on rocky slopes. Areas 13, 15, 16, 17, ?18 (and in Iraq, Iran, Afghanistan, Pakistan, Kashmir and USSR).

F. latakiensis Rix in *Kew Bull.* 30: 161 (1975)

About 10–25 cm in height. Leaves alternate, linear. Flowers one to two, narrowly campanulate, purple outside, greenish-yellow inside. Style deeply three-lobed, glabrous. In scrub and woodland. Areas 7, ?8 (and in N. Syria).

F. latifolia Willd., *Sp. Pl.* 2, 1: 92 (1799) (Turkish name: Benekli lâle)

A robust species about 15–30 cm in height. Leaves alternate, broad, grey-green. Flowers large, broadly campanulate, chocolate-brown, tessellated, about 2.5–3.5 cm diameter. Style three-lobed. Rocky places. Areas 4, ?12, 13, 14 (and in Caucasus).

 The yellow, brown-tessellated *F. lutea* M. Bieb. from the Caucasus is very similar except for its flower colour. *F. nobilis* Baker is like a dwarf form of *F. latifolia* with huge chocolate or purple-brown bells up to 4 cm diameter, often carried on such short stems as to be resting on the ground. However they are not always dwarf and there is an overlap in size with *F. latifolia*. It may thus be best to regard *F. nobilis* as a mountain form of *F. latifolia*. Recorded from areas 4, ?13, 14.

F. michailovskyi Fomin in Monit. Jard. Bot. Tiflis 1: 18 (1905)

About 7–15 cm in height. Leaves alternate, grey-green. Flowers broadly campanulate, bicoloured, the basal half to two-thirds metallic purple or purple-brown, the upper part bright yellow, about 2–2.5 cm diameter. Style three-lobed. Alpine turf and stony places. Areas ?4, ?13, 14, 15 (endemic).

F. minima Rix in Notes from Roy. Bot. Gard. Edinb. 31, 1: 12 (1971)

About 5–8 cm in height. Leaves alternate, green. Flowers solitary, yellow, narrowly campanulate-conical, up to 1.5 cm diameter. Style three-lobed. Areas 13, 15, 16 (endemic).

F. minuta Boiss. & Noë in Boiss., Diagn. Pl. Or. Nov. Ser. 2, 4: 104 (1859) (Syn. F. carduchorum Rix)

Plant 5–12 cm in height. Leaves alternate, bright shiny green. Flowers usually solitary, narrowly campanulate, reddish-brown or orange-brown, up to 1.5 cm diameter. Style deeply three-lobed at apex. In short turf or stony slopes. Areas 13, 14, 15, 16 (and in N.W. Iran)

F. persica L., Sp. Pl.: 304 (1753)

Tall plant 20–100 cm in height. Leaves many, alternate, grey-green. Flowers seven to 20 in raceme, campanulate-conical, pale to deep purple or purplish-maroon, often glaucous on the outside, up to 2 cm diameter. Style slender, entire. Fields, rocky hillsides and edge of woods. Areas 8, ?13, 17 (and in Syria, Iraq, Israel and Iran).

In parts of its range F. persica can have flowers coloured brown or straw-yellow but these do not apparently occur in Turkey.

F. pinardii Boiss., Diagn. Pl. Or. Nov. Ser. 1, 7: 106 (1846). (Syn. F. syriaca Hayek & Siehe)

About 10–15 cm tall. Leaves alternate, grey-green. Flowers solitary, narrowly campanulate-conical, purple or brown-purple with a glaucous exterior, yellow or greenish inside, up to 1.5 cm diameter; the segments usually curve outwards at their tips. Style slender, entire or three-lobed. Stony places. Areas 2, 6–13, 16, 17, 18 (and in Caucasus, Syria, Lebanon).

F. pontica Wahlenb. in Berggren, Resor 2: Bihang 27 (1826)

About 20–40 cm in height. Leaves grey-green, alternate in weak specimens, opposite or occasionally whorled in vigorous plants; the upper three always whorled and exceeding the flower. Flowers one to two, broadly campanulate, green with brownish margins and tips to the segments, not tessellated, 2.5–3 cm in diameter. Style three-lobed. In woods. Areas 1, 2, 3, 5 (and in Greece, Bulgaria and Aegean Is.).

F. sibthorpiana (Sibthorp & Smith) Baker in Jour. Linn. Soc. 14: 275 (1874)

About 20–30 cm in height. Leaves alternate, only two on each stem, the lower rather broad, grey-green. Flower solitary, narrowly campanulate, yellow, up to 1 cm wide at the mouth. Style entire, rather thick. Rocky places in Pinus brutia woods. Area 6 (endemic).

***F. straussii* Bornm. in *Mitt. Thur. Bot. Ver.* 20: 45 (1904)**
About 10–15 cm in height. Leaves shiny green, rather broad, usually opposite or whorled. Flowers one to four, broadly campanulate, green or brownish, distinctly tessellated, about 2–2.5 cm diameter. Style deeply three-lobed. In scrub and on rocky slopes. Area 16 (and in W. Iran).

***F. stribrnyi* Velen., in *Sitz.-Ber. Böhm. Ges. Wiss.* 37: 61 (1893)**
About 10–30 cm tall. Leaves many, green, narrowly linear or narrowly lanceolate, the upper in a whorl of three around the flower. Flowers one to three, narrowly campanulate, dull purple with a green stripe along each segment or greenish with the segments edged dull purple, not tessellated, about 1 cm diameter. In scrub. Area 1 (and in Bulgaria).

***F. subalpina* Siehe in Hayek, *Ann. Naturk. Mus. Wien* 28: 183 (1914)**
This name applies to a Siehe collection from Konya Vilayet, near Ereğli in the Bulgar Dağ. It was said to have been purple flowered with the upper leaves in whorls of three.

***F. uva-vulpis* Rix in *Kew Bull.* 29, 4: 651 (1974)**
About 10–20 cm tall. Leaves alternate, shiny green. Flowers solitary, narrowly campanulate, purple with a glaucous exterior, the segments tipped with yellow, not tessellated, up to 1.5 cm diameter. Style thick, entire. In fields. Area 13 (and in N.W. Iran and N. Iraq).

***F. viridiflora* Post in *Bull. Herb. Boiss.* 3: 164 (1895)**
About 10–25 cm tall. Leaves alternate, slightly glaucous, the upper in a whorl of three. Flowers one to two, narrowly campanulate-conical, green, up to 2 cm diameter. Style slender, entire. Stony fields. Area 8 (endemic).
    This is rather like *F. alfredae* subsp. *glaucoviridis*, but has a slender style and larger, wider, flowers.

***F. whittallii* Baker in *Gard. Chron.* Ser. 3, 13: 506 (1893)**
About 15–30 cm in height. Leaves alternate, narrowly linear, grey-green. Flowers one to two, broadly campanulate, green with distinct brown tessellation, 2.5–3 cm diameter. Style deeply three-lobed. Stony or rocky places in the open or in coniferous woods. Area 7 (endemic).

***F. zagrica* Stapf in *Verh. Zool.-Bot. Ges. Wien* 38: 551 (1888)**
About 5–12 cm in height. Leaves alternate or the lowest opposite, lanceolate, grey-green. Flowers one to two, narrowly campanulate, dark purple-brown with yellow tips to segments and sometimes a yellow median stripe on each. Style rather slender, obscurely three-lobed, papillose. Rocky places. Area 16 (and in W. Iran).

6 *Gagea* (Turkish: Altın yıldız)

Small bulbous plants with one or two small bulbs inside a tunic and with many small bulbils. Leaves basal and cauline, usually filiform or narrowly linear. Flowers solitary or few in an umbel or raceme. Perianth segments six, free, yellow or greenish with a green or dark stripe on the outside of each segment, or occasionally white. Stamens six. Capsule three angled with three locules. Seeds flat or globose to ovoid.

This is a genus of perhaps 100 species, but their taxonomy is not yet fully understood and there may be much re-adjustment of names and numbers of species when the whole genus is revised. In Turkey there are about 26 species. They are all spring-flowering, usually inhabiting mountain meadows or rocky hillsides.

The Turkish species are all yellowish-flowered except for *G. graeca* which has nodding white flowers.

The small starry yellow-flowered gageas are hardly known in cultivation although they can be cultivated in an alpine house or bulb frame without difficulty. Mostly they are not showy enough to be of garden value but the one white-flowered species, *G. graeca*, with its pendent white bells is attractive.

G. bohemica (Zauschner) Schultes, *Syst. Veg.* 7: 549 (1829) (Syn. *G. szovitsii* (Láng) Besser, *G. smyrnaea* O. Schwarz)

A very compact plant. Basal leaves two, thread-like, about 1 mm wide, longer than the flower stem. Stem usually 2–5 cm tall, normally hairy in the upper part. Flowers one to three, yellow inside, green outside, with blunt segments 1–1.5 cm long. Rocky places. Areas 1, 2, 3, 4, 5, 6, 7, 8, 9, 11, 13, 17 (and widespread in Europe).

G. bulbifera (Pallas) Schultes, *Syst. Veg.* 7: 552 (1829)

Basal leaves one to two, thread-like, 1–2 mm wide; one bulbil usually present in the axil of each stem leaf. Stems 5–15 cm tall, greyish-hairy. Flowers on long pedicels, one to three, yellow with a green stripe on the outside of each segment; segments acute, about 1 cm long, greyish-hairy. Stony places. Areas 4, 12, 13, 14, 15 (and eastwards to W. China).

G. chlorantha (M. Bieb.) Schultes, *Syst. Veg.* 7: 551 (1829) (Syn. *G. damascena* Boiss. & Gaill.)

Basal leaves two, only 1 mm wide, hairy, shorter than the flower stem. Stems 5–20 cm tall, finely hairy. Flowers two to five, yellow inside, green outside, with blunt segments 1–2 cm long. Dry rocky places. Areas 8, 13, 17, 18 (and in W. Asia east to Russian C. Asia).

C. chrysantha (Jan) Schultes, *Syst. Veg.* 7: 545 (1829) (Syn. *G. ambylopetala* Boiss. & Heldr.)

Basal leaves two, channelled, much longer than the flower stem, 1.5–2.5 mm wide. Stem about 3–10 cm tall, glabrous. Flowers one to seven, yellow, often brownish-red outside, with blunt segments about 1 cm long. Stony places and in scrub. Areas 1, 3, 5, 6 (and in Balkans, Italy and N. Africa).

G. bithynica Pascher is very similar in its characters but the basal leaves are only 1–2 mm wide and are equal to or shorter than the flower stem; the perianth segments are acute. Wet places. Areas 2, 5, 6, 7, 9 (endemic).

G. tenera Pascher is similar in its characters to *G. chrysantha* but has thread-like leaves less than 1 mm wide; the stems are slightly hairy. Damp places. Area 15 (and in Iran, east to Russian C. Asia).

G. tenuissima Miscz. is similar in its characters to *G. chrysantha* but has thread-like basal leaves only 1 mm wide; the stem leaves are opposite, not alternate, as in *G. chrysantha*. Stony places. Area 4 (endemic).

G. confusa Terracc. in *Boll. Soc. Ort. Palermo* 2, 3: 5 (1904)

Basal leaf solitary, flat, about 2–4 mm wide, longer than the flower stem. Stem 5–15 cm tall, glabrous. Flowers usually one to five, yellow inside, brownish or green outside, with blunt segments about 1–1.5 cm long. Near the snowline high in the mountains. Areas ?11, 15, 16 (and in Iraq, Iran and Russia).

G. fibrosa (Desf.) Schultes, *Syst. Veg.* 7: 552 (1829) (Syn. *G. rigida* Boiss.)

Basal leaf usually solitary, flat, 2–4 mm wide, longer than flower stems. Stem less than 10 cm tall, finely hairy. Flowers often solitary but sometimes up to five, yellow inside, green outside, with long-pointed segments 1.5–2.5 cm long. Dry rocky places, often in scrub. Areas 7, 8, 17 (and in Aegean Is., Cyprus, Russia and Iran).

G. fistulosa (Ramond ex DC.) Ker-Gawler in *Journ. Sci. Arts* (London) 1: 180 (1816) (Syn. *G. liotardii* (Sternb.) Schultes, *G. anisanthos* K. Koch)

Basal leaf solitary, hollow, 2–5 mm wide, equal to or longer than the flower stem. Stem 5–15 cm, glabrous. Flowers two to five, yellow, with obtuse segments 1–2 cm long. Damp grassy places. Areas 2, 3, 4, 5, 6, 7, 8, 11, 12, 13, 14, 15 (and widespread in Europe and the Middle East).

This differs from *G. luteoides* in having the head of flowers arising directly from the axils of the upper stem leaves, with no intervening stem.

G. glacialis K. Koch is very similar to *G. fistulosa* but the flower is usually solitary, rarely two, and the segments are up to 1.2 cm long. Areas 4, 8, 11, 12, 13, 14, 15 (and in Caucasus and Iran).

G. foliosa (J. & C. Presl) Schultes, *Syst. Veg.* 7: 1703 (1830)

Basal leaves two, flat, 2–5 mm wide, equal in length to or longer than the flower stem. Stems 2–7 cm tall, hairy in the upper part. Flowers one to five, yellow, with pointed segments 1–1.7 cm long. Grassy places and light woodland. Areas 2, 6, 7 (and the Mediterranean region).

G. gageoides (Zucc.) Vved. in *Fl. Turkmen.* 1: 261 (1932)

Basal leaf solitary or sometimes absent, flat, about 1 mm wide, equal in length to the flower stem. Stems wiry, flexuose, about 5–15 cm tall, with bulbils in the leaf axils, glabrous. Flowers one per stem, pale yellow, with blunt segments only 5–8 mm long. Rocky places. Areas 8, 10, 11, 13, 15, 16, 17, 18 (and in Caucasus and Iran, east to Russian C. Asia).

G. graeca (L.) Terracc. in *Mém. Soc. Bot. Fr.* 2: 25 (1905). (Syn. *Lloydia graeca* (L.) Endl. ex Kunth)

Basal leaves two, narrowly linear, flat, about 1–2 mm wide, shorter than the flower stem. Stem 5–10 cm tall, glabrous. Flowers one to five, pendulous or horizontal, widely funnel-shaped or campanulate, white with purple veins on the obtuse segments which are 0.5–1.5 cm long. Rocky places. Areas 6, ?7 (and in Greece and Crete).

G. granatellii (Parl.) Parl., *Fl. Palerm.* 1: 376 (1845). (Syn. *G. pinardii* Terracc., *G. dubia* Terracc.)

Basal leaves two, flat, 2–4 mm wide, longer than the flower stems. Stem 6–12 cm tall, finely hairy or glabrous. Bulbils usually present in the stem leaf axils. Flowers three to 13, yellow, with pointed, hairy segments 1–2 cm long. Rocky places and in scrub. Areas 2, 3, 4, 6, 7, 8, 9, 10, 11, 12, 13, 18 (and widespread in the Mediterranean region).

G. helenae Grossh. in Grossh. & Schischkin, *Pl. Or. Exs.* fasc. 1, 8: 21 (1924)

Basal leaf solitary, 3–4 mm wide, flat, longer than the flower stem. Stems 5–10 cm long, glabrous. Flowers two to eight, yellow inside, green outside, with blunt segments 1–2 cm long. Rocky places. Area 15 (and in Caucasus).

    G. chanae Grossh. is similar in its characters to *G. helenae* but has hairy stems and greyish hairy leaves. Areas 14, 15 (and in Caucasus).

G. luteoides Stapf in *Denkschr. Akad. Wiss. Wien*, Math.-Nat. Kl. 50: 8 (1885) (Syn. *G. joannis* Grossh., *G. linearifolia* Terracc., *G. sintenisii* Pascher, *G. syriaca* Terracc.)

Basal leaf solitary, hollow, 2–4 mm wide, longer than the flower stem. Stem 5–10 cm, glabrous or hairy. Flowers two to six, pale yellow, with acute segments 1–1.5 cm long. Stony or grassy places. Areas 4, 8, 11, 12, 13, 14, 15 (and in Caucasus and Iran).

    G. luteoides differs from *G. fistulosa* in having the cluster of flowers carried on a short stem above the stem leaves.

G. peduncularis (J. & C. Presl) Pascher in *Sitz.-Ber. Deutsch. Naturw.-Med. Ver. Böhm.*, Lotos, n.s. 24: 114 (1904)

Basal leaves two, flat, 1–2 mm wide, longer than the flower stem. Stems 5–15 cm, usually hairy, sometimes glabrous. Flowers one to four, on long slender densely hairy pedicels, with blunt segments 1.1–1.5 cm long. Rocky places. Areas 1, 5, 6, 7, 8 (and in Balkans, Cyprus, N. Africa).

    G. juliae Pascher is rather similar in characters but the pedicels are only slightly hairy and the segments are usually about 1 cm long. In or near woods. Areas 7, 8 (and in Cyprus).

G. pratensis (Pers.) Dumort., *Fl. Belg.* 140 (1827)

Basal leaf solitary, flat or channelled, 2–4 mm wide, equalling or overtopping the flowers. Stem up to 10 cm tall, glabrous. Flowers one to four, yellow inside, green outside, with acute segments about 1–2 cm long. Scrub and light woodland. Areas 1, 5, 6 (and widespread in Europe).

G. reticulata (Pallas) Schultes, *Syst. Veg.* 7: 542 (1829). (Syn. *G. tenuifolia* (Boiss.) Fomin)

Plants often forming clumps. Bulbs with a netted collar 1–5 cm long. Basal leaf solitary, overtopping the flower stems, only 1 mm wide. Stems 5–15 cm tall, finely hairy. Flowers two to four, yellow inside, green outside, with long-pointed segments 1.5–2 cm long. Dryish stony places. Areas 12, 13, 14, 17 (and in N. Africa, Syria, Iran, USSR).

G. taurica Steven is similar to *C. reticulata* but has no collar to the bulb and has leaves up to 3 mm wide. Stony places. Areas 8, 10, 11, 12, 13, 14, 15, 16 (and widespread in W. and C. Asia).

G. uliginosa Siehe & Pascher in *Sitz.-Ber. Deutsch. Naturw.-Med. Ver.* Böhm. Lotos, n.s. 24: 129 (1904)

Bulb with a collar up to 2 cm long. Basal leaf solitary, 1–1.5 mm wide, shorter than the flowers. Stems only 3–5 cm tall, glabrous. Flowers bright yellow, brownish-red outside, solitary (rarely two) with acute segments 1–1.5 cm long. Damp places high in the mountains. Areas 8, 10, 13, 15, 16 (and in N. Iraq and Iran).

G. villosa (M. Bieb.) Duby, *Bot. Gall.* 1: 467 (1828) (Syn. *G. arvensis* (Pers.) Dumort, *G. boissieri* Pascher)

Basal leaves two, semicylindrical, 1–2.5 mm wide, longer than the flower stems; bulbils sometimes present in axils. Stem 1–10 cm tall, hairy or glabrous. Flowers up to 15, yellow, with blunt segments 0.7–2 cm long. Rocky places, fields and open hillsides. Areas 1–16 (and widespread in Europe, N. Africa and W. Asia).

7 *Hyacinthella*

A small genus of about 16 species of very dwarf bulbous plants, the bulbs usually recognizable by the whitish powder (crystals) which adheres to the tunics. Leaves two or three basal, usually with very prominent fibre strands, especially when dried. Flowers usually in dense to rather loose racemes, campanulate or tubular with six short lobes, pale blue to deep violet-blue. Fruit a three-valved capsule with globose blackish seeds. The perianth remains attached at the base during the fruiting stage, whereas in *Bellevalia* and *Muscari* it becomes detached rather soon after flowering time.

In Turkey there are nine species. They have at times been included in *Bellevalia* and *Hyacinthus*. They flower in April to June.

This small group of diminutive plants has been almost neglected by gardeners although most of them are brightly coloured and of as much decorative value as the grape hyacinths. As alpine house plants they are easy to grow and their blue-to-violet flowers can be appreciated at close quarters.

H. acutiloba K. Persson & Wendelbo in *Candollea* 36: 524 (1981)

Leaves 10–25 mm wide, glabrous but with a ciliate margin. Flowers about 5–7 mm long, pale to mid blue in rather loose racemes on pedicels 2–6 mm long. Limestone slopes in scrub. Areas 11, 12, 13 (endemic).

H. campanulata K. Persson & Wendelbo in *Candollea* 36: 522 (1981)

Leaves 6–15 mm wide, glabrous. Flowers about 5 mm long, pale blue in rather loose racemes on pedicels 1.5–3 mm long. Stony places. Area 10 (endemic).

H. glabrescens (Boiss.) K. Persson & Wendelbo in *Candollea* 36: 520 (1981). (Syn. *H. hispida* var. *glabrescens* Boiss., *H. lineata* var. *glabrescens* (Boiss.) Feinbr.)

Leaves 8–20 mm wide, glabrous; margin smooth. Flowers about 5–6 mm long, deep violet-blue, in rather loose racemes on pedicels 2–7 mm long. Dry rocky slopes. Area 8 (endemic).

H. heldreichii (Boiss.) Chouard in *Bull. Mus. Nat. Hist. Nat. Paris* Ser. 2, 3: 178 (1931)

Leaves about 5–10 mm broad, glabrous. Flowers about 5–6 mm long, deep violet-blue, more or less sessile in a dense spike or sometimes on short pedicels less than 2 mm long. Rocky places. Areas 7, 8, 10 (endemic).

H. hispida (Gay) Chouard in *Bull. Mus. Nat. Hist. Nat. Paris* Ser. 2, 3: 178 (1931)

Leaves 5–15 mm broad, covered with long wispy hairs. Flowers about 5–6 mm long, deep blue, in rather loose racemes, on pedicels about 2–4 mm long. Rocky mountain slopes. Area 8 (endemic).

H. lineata (Steudel) Chouard in *Bull. Mus. Nat. Hist. Nat. Paris* Ser. 2, 3: 178 (1931)

Leaves about 5–15 mm broad, glabrous, or sometimes pubescent below; margin ciliate. Flowers about 5 mm long, deep blue, in rather loose racemes, on pedicels about 3–6 mm long. Stony places usually in mountains. Areas 2, 6, 7, 9 (endemic).

H. micrantha (Boiss.) Chouard in *Bull. Mus. Nat. Hist. Nat. Paris* Ser. 2, 3: 178 (1931)

Leaves usually only 2–4 mm broad, glabrous or minutely pubescent on underside. Flowers very small, usually 3–4 mm long, pale blue or whitish, sessile, in a very short dense spike. Stony slopes. Areas 2, 3, 9, 11 (endemic). The tiniest species, easily overlooked. The leaves have no raised nerves, unlike most other species.

K. Persson & Wendelbo in *Candollea* 36: 537 (1981) consider that this species hybridizes with *H. heldreichii* in Area 8. These hybrids probably account for records of *H. millingenii* (Post) Feinbr. in Turkey which is similar in appearance to the hybrid. *H. millingenii* which occurs in Cyprus.

H. nervosa (Bertol.) Chouard in *Bull. Mus. Nat. Hist. Nat. Paris* Ser. 2, 3: 178 (1931)

Leaves 5–20 mm broad, with a finely ciliate margin. Flowers 7–9 mm long, pale blue, more or less sessile in a dense raceme. Rocky places. Area 17 (and in Israel, Jordan, Iraq, Lebanon and Syria). This is easily recognized by the long rather bright but pale blue flowers.

H. siirtensis B. Mathew in *Kew Bull.* 28, 3: 517 (1973)

Leaves 5–13 mm broad, glabrous but with a finely ciliate margin. Flowers

5–8 mm long, rather irregular in shape, pale blue, sessile, in a short spike. Dry stony hills. Areas 17, 18. This is the only species known to occur in the extreme east of Turkey.

8 *Hyacinthus* (English: Hyacinth; Turkish: Sümbül)

Popular garden plants the cultivars of which are all derived from one species, *H. orientalis*.

Bulb large, usually with dark purple papery tunics. Leaves in a basal cluster, linear or narrowly lanceolate. Scape carrying a loose raceme of infundibuliform or tubular flowers which have six spreading or recurved lobes about as long as the tube. Stamens inserted in the lower part of the tube. Style short with a capitate stigma. Fruit rather fleshy, globose, three locular with several blackish seeds in each locule.

A genus of only three species in west and central Asia. In Turkey there is one species.

The horticultural value of this well-known plant is enormous and hyacinth bulb production is a large industry, especially in Holland. All the garden cultivars presently available have been selected, over hundreds of years, from the native Turkish species. The wild form is as easily cultivated as the garden forms and, although less showy, is perhaps more graceful.

H. orientalis L., Sp. Pl: 454 (1753) subsp. *orientalis*

Flowers funnel-shaped or nearly tubular with recurved lobes which are shorter than the tube, pale to mid blue or rarely white, very sweetly scented, two to 15 in a raceme. April–May. Rocky slopes in mountains up to 1,600 metres altitude. Areas 8, 17 (and in Syria and Lebanon).

Turkish people are very fond of this species for its fragrance. In Ottoman times, in Istanbul, many cultivars were raised in white, blue, yellow and pink forms, both double and single. In the Topkapı palace library there is a book[147] showing illustrations of some of the cultivated forms of this period. Forty-two forms are recorded in colour.

Subsp. *chionophilus* Wendelbo differs from subsp. *orientalis* in having broader leaves, 1.2–3.6 cm wide (usually only 4–5 mm wide in subsp. *orientalis*); the lobes of the perianth are as long as the tube in subsp. *chionophilus*. Rocky places, often near melting snow, 1,600–2,500 metres. Areas 8, 12, 13 (endemic).

9 *Lilium* (English: Lily; Turkish: Zambak)

A large genus of about 80 species of beautiful plants distributed throughout temperate and warm temperate areas of the northern hemisphere.

Bulb ovoid, scaly, yellowish or white. Flowers funnel-shaped or bell-shaped with six recurving perianth segments which are not joined. Stamens six, often protruding from the perianth on long slender filaments. Style very long, with a thick three-lobed stigma. Fruit a three-valved capsule with numerous flat seeds.

In Turkey there are six species – for more information see P. H. Davis, 'A Revision of Turkish Lilies' in *The Lily Year Book 1970*: 212 (1969).

Turkish lilies flower in mid to late summer, usually June–July.

Except for *L. candidum*, the Turkish lilies do not compare with the eastern Asiatic species in beauty and are rare in gardens. The northern yellow species are nevertheless attractive and worthy of cultivation but require a cool moist atmosphere if they are to succeed. *L. candidum* by contrast needs hot sun and good drainage.

L. candidum L., Sp. Pl. 1: 302 (1753). (English: Madonna Lily; Turkish: Ak zambak)

The only white-flowered Turkish species. Basal leaves overwintering, forming a rosette which dies away at flowering time. Flower stem 1–1.5 metres tall, densely covered with erect leaves in the lower part. Flowers widely bell-shaped, white and sweetly scented. Rocky places and in light woodland. Areas 6, 7, 8 (and in Greece and other Eastern Mediterranean countries).

The Madonna Lily has been cultivated for many centuries and it is now difficult to say where it is a native. It occurs in apparently wild situations in southern Turkey at low altitudes in maquis and light woodland.

L. ciliatum P. Davis in Notes Roy. Bot. Gard. Edinb. 28: 235 (1965)

This unusual lily grows to about 1–1.5 metres in height with a very densely leafy stem, the leaves bright green but with long silvery hairs on the margins. Flower-buds densely hairy. The one to several small pendulous flowers are pale primrose-yellow or creamy, with a blackish-purple centre and have the segments rolled right back to touch the greenish tube. Subalpine slopes in thickets and light woodland. Area 4 (endemic).

L. kesselringianum Miscz. in Trudy Prikl. Bot. 7: 251 (1914)

Similar to *L. szovitsianum* (see below) but flowers cream to straw-yellow with purplish spots in the throat. The segments are long and narrow with very acute tips. Wooded hills and meadows. Area 4, in Artvin district (and in W. Georgian SSR).

L. martagon L., Sp. Pl. 1: 303 (1753). Syn. L. caucasicum Miscz. (The Martagon Lily; Turkish: Kırmızı zambak)

A robust species 1–2 metres in height with numerous dark green leaves in whorls up the stem. The ten to 50 flowers are carried in a raceme and are pendulous with strongly revolute segments of a dull pinkish-purple with dark spots. Deciduous woodland at low altitudes. Areas 1, 2 (widespread in Europe, east to Siberia). The bulbs of this species are used medicinally as a vesicant and diuretic.

L. ponticum K. Koch in Linnaea 22: 234 (1849)

This is very similar to *L. ciliatum* described above, but does not have the long silvery hairs on the leaves and flower-buds and has deeper yellow flowers. Meadows and mountain woodlands. Area 4, mountains above Rize and Trabzon (and in Georgian SSR).

L. ponticum is very closely allied to the two European species *L. pyrenaicum* and *L. carniolicum* and is now treated by Davis & Henderson as a subspecies of the latter.

Var. *artvinense* (Miscz.) P. Davis & Henderson differs in having a more slender habit and fawn-orange flowers. Area 4 (endemic to the Artvin area).

L. szovitsianum Fischer & Avé-Lall., *Index Sem. Horti Petrop.* 58 (1838)

A very vigorous lily up to 2 metres in height with numerous scattered leaves. The large rich yellow pendulous flowers number one to 25 in a dense raceme and are bell-shaped with outward-curving segments giving a flower diameter of up to 10 cm. Edge of woodland and in scrub on acid soils. ? Area 4, reported from Kars (and in adjacent USSR).

Var. *armenum* Miscz. differs in having smaller, more acute, inner perianth segments (10–16 mm broad) than in var. *szovitsianum* (18–22 mm broad) in which they are obtuse. Area 4, in mountains above Trabzon and Ordu (and in Armenian SSR).

10 *Merendera*

A small genus, closely related to and resembling *Colchicum* and differing only in having no perianth tube, the segments being free from each other nearly to the base. For the rest of the description, see *Colchicum*.

There are about ten species, mainly in western Asia. In Turkey, four or five species occur, flowering March to June, although *M. attica* occasionally flowers in winter or even late autumn.

Records for the central Asiatic *M. raddeana* Regel in Turkey probably refer to *M. trigyna*.

Most of the species are of little horticultural value since their flimsy flowers lack substance and are damaged by inclement weather. They can be cultivated in an alpine house or bulb frame without difficulty and one species with larger more showy flowers, *M. kurdica*, is well worth growing in this way.

M. attica Boiss. & Spruner, *Diagn. Pl. Or. Nov.* Ser. 1, 5: 67 (1844)

Leaves usually three, linear-lanceolate, about 4–6 mm wide. Flowers several, white or pale pinkish-lilac with very narrow segments. Open stony hills and in scrub. Areas 5, 6, 7 (and in Greece).

A very common plant in W. Turkey, easily recognized by its spidery flowers which shrivel and remain attached to the developing fruit. The corm tunics are blackish and ribbed.

M. kurdica Bornm. in *Bull. Herb. Boiss.* 7: 79 (1899)

The most attractive species in the genus with broad glossy green leaves and comparatively large goblet-shaped deep pink flowers with wide, overlapping perianth segments. Mountain slopes. Areas 15, 16 (also in W. Iran and N.E. Iraq).

M. navis-noae Markgraf in *Kulturpfl.* Beiheft 3: 34 (1962)

Leaves two, strap-like with a blunt apex, 1–2 cm wide, glabrous. Flowers solitary, lilac, with segments 1.5–3 cm long, 0.6–1 cm wide. Area 14 (endemic).

This was described from Mt Ararat (hence the name *navis-noae* = Noah's Boat) from a collection made on 17 April 1957 by Dr Sauer. It is obviously very similar to *M. trigyna* and may be synonymous.

M. sobolifera Fischer & C. Meyer, *Ind. Sem. Hort. Petrop.* 1: 34 (1835)

This is the only species which has a slender horizontal soboliferous corm. It is a small plant, usually with two to three grey-green leaves and a purple-tinged leaf sheath. Flowers one to two, white or pale mauve with long narrow segments. Damp grassy places. Areas 1, 5, ?6, 13, 15 (and in Iran and Russia).

M. trigyna (Adams) Woronow in *Acta Horti Petrop.* 28: 431 (1910). (Syn: *M. caucasica* M. Bieb.)

Leaves usually two to three, linear-lanceolate. Flowers one to three, white or mauve-pink, with segments much broader than in *M. attica* giving a substantial Crocus-shaped flower. Alpine turf and screes, usually near snow patches, 2,000–3,500 metres. Areas 3, 4, 11, 12, 13, 14, 15 (and in Iran and Caucasus).

M. manissadjianii Azn. in *Bull. Herb. Boiss.* 7: 248 (1908) was described from material collected on Tavşan Dağ near Merzifon in May 1907 by J. J. Manissadjian. It is very like *M. trigyna*.

11 *Muscari* (English: Grape Hyacinth; Turkish: Arapsümbülü, Morbaş)

Small bulbous plants with linear or linear-lanceolate basal leaves and spikes or racemes of blue, brownish or yellowish flowers. Perianth tubular or globose with six very short lobes, or 'teeth' as they are often called. These may be a different colour from the perianth tube and this should be noted for identification purposes. Fruit a three-valved capsule containing black, wrinkled seeds.

A genus of about 40 species, mainly distributed in the Mediterranean region but extending into Russia and Iran. In Turkey there are about 18 species.

The genera *Leopoldia*, *Muscarimia* and *Pseudomuscari* are included here with *Muscari*. All are spring- or early summer-flowering, except for *M. paviflorum*.

In gardens grape hyacinths have the reputation of being weedy and indeed certain species, such as *M. neglectum* and *M. armeniacum*, can become invasive. Such species are best for naturalizing under shrubs. Others such as *M. aucheri*, *M. azureum* and the yellow *M. macrocarpum* are less prolific and are most attractive subjects for the rock garden or alpine house.

M. armeniacum Leichtlin ex Baker in *Gard. Chron.* 9: 798 (1878)

Leaves usually greyish-green and channelled on the upper surface. Flowers bright sky-blue or slightly mauve-blue, in dense racemes which become more lax with age. Perianth obovoid or oblong, strongly contracted at the mouth, with white or pale blue 'teeth'. Grassy or stony places, sometimes in scrub. Widespread in Turkey (and in E. Balkans and Caucasus).

   M. szovitsianum Baker is best regarded as a variant of this. *M. sintenisii* Freyn is probably also a synonym, as is *M. polyanthum* Boiss., described from Erciyes Dağ and the Taurus. *M. maweanum* hort ex Baker also looks similar to *M. armeniacum*. Records for the Balkan *M. botryoides* (L.) Miller in Turkey are probably misidentifications of *M. armeniacum*.

M. aucheri (Boiss.) Baker in *Jour. Linn. Soc.* 11: 418 (1871) (Syn. *M. lingulatum* Baker)

Leaves rather short and wide with a blunt tip, greyish-green. Flowers bright blue, the upper sterile ones often paler, produced in a short dense raceme. Perianth globose, with white 'teeth', strongly contracted at the mouth. Alpine meadows, often near melting snow. Areas 2, 3, 4, 6, 8, 9, 12, 13 (endemic).

M. azureum Fenzl in *Ann. Sci. Nat.* Ser. 4, 12: 165 (1859)

Leaves rather short at flowering time, very grey-green on the upper surface, widest towards the apex. Flowers bright sky-blue, in a dense raceme. Perianth campanulate, not constricted, the lobes or teeth often with a darker blue mid-vein. Alpine meadows near melting snow. Areas 3, 4, 8, 12, 13, 14 (endemic).

M. bourgaei Baker in *Jour. Linn. Soc.* 11: 416 (1871)

Leaves rather short and only 4–6 mm wide with a whitish line running along the centre. Flowers brilliant mid-blue, in a short dense raceme. Perianth oblong, with whitish 'teeth', strongly contracted at the mouth. Alpine turf near melting snow. Areas 2, 5, 6, 7 (endemic).

   M. schliemannii Freyn & Asch. from Kaz Dağ looks very like this and may be synonymous.

M. caucasicum (Griseb.) Baker in *Jour. Linn. Soc.*11: 414 (1871)

This is very similar to *M. comosum* (see below) but the upper sterile flowers are on rather short pedicels and are almost equal in length to the fertile flowers. Dry stony hills and fields. Areas 14, ?15 (and in N. Iran and Caucasus).

M. coeleste Fomin in *Monit. Jard. Bot. Tiflis* 9: 11 (1908)

This is rather similar to *M. azureum* but has very pale blue flowers and more or less parallel-sided leaves, not wider towards the apex. Alpine meadows. Area 14 (and in S. Caucasus).

M. comosum (L.) Miller, *Gard. Dict.* ed. 8, no. 2 (1768) (Turkish name: Dağ soğanı)

A tall species, up to 50 cm. Leaves linear, up to 2.5 cm wide, greyish or purplish-green. Flowers brownish, in long loose racemes. Perianth oblong-urceolate, up to 1 cm long, with creamy or yellowish teeth, strongly contracted at the mouth. Sterile (upper) flowers bluish-violet, on long violet upright pedicels. In fields and dry grassy places. Widespread in Turkey (and throughout most of Europe, east to Russia). The bulbs of this species are tinged with pink. It flowers in early summer.

M. discolor Boiss. & Hausskn. in Boiss., Fl. Or. 5: 300 (1884)
Leaves narrowly linear. Flowers deep blue with white teeth, produced in a fairly dense raceme. Perianth narrowly tubular, not constricted at the mouth. In mountains, in rocky or grassy places. Areas ?17, ?18 (endemic).

M. latifolium Kirk in Edinb. New Phil. Journ. n.s. 7: 317 (1858)
A robust species with one broad grey-green oblanceolate leaf. Flowers dark, almost blackish-blue in a dense raceme. Perianth oblong, strongly contracted at the mouth, with the teeth the same colour as the tube. Open pinewoods. Areas 5, 6 (endemic).

M. longipes Boiss., Diagn. Pl. Or. Nov. Ser. 1, 13: 36 (1853)
Similar to M. comosum (see above) but with blackish 'teeth' (perianth lobes) to the flower. After flowering the pedicels elongate enormously, unlike the related M. tenuiflorum in which they remain short. Mountain slopes. Areas 8, 9, 10, 11, ?12, ?13, ?15, ?16, 17, 18 (and in Iraq, Israel and Caucasus).

M. macrocarpum Sweet, Brit. Fl. Gard. Ser. 1, 3: t. 210 (1827)
Bulb large, with perennial fleshy white roots. Leaves about 1–1.5 cm wide at the base and long-tapering, very glaucous. Flowers yellow, very sweetly scented, nearly tubular, in dense spikes. Perianth contracted at the mouth, with a brownish rim. Rocky places at low altitudes. Areas 6, 7 (and in Greek Is.).

M. massayanum Grunert in Gartenwelt 35: 205 (1931)
This is similar to M. comosum but the buds and sterile flowers are pinkish and the open flowers yellowish; the pedicels are shorter. Rocky slopes. Area 8 (endemic).

M. microstomum P. Davis & Stuart in R.H.S. Lily Year Book 30: 124 (1966)
Leaves rather broad, 6–10 mm. wide, with a white line along the centre. Flowers blue, in a rather dense raceme which becomes loose at the end of the flowering time. Perianth oblong, with pale 'teeth', very constricted at the mouth. Rocky places. Area 8 (endemic).

M. muscarimi Medicus in Usteri, Ann. Bot. 2: 15 (1791). (Syn. M. moschatum Willd.) (Turkish name: Misk soğanı)
This is similar to M. macrocarpum but has greenish or whitish flowers which are slightly narrower. Rocky places. Areas 7, 8 (said to be in Caucasus also).

A plant somewhat similar to and probably a variant of this is cultivated under the name M. ambrosiacum; it has white flowers flushed pale lavender.

M. neglectum Guss. in Tenore, Fl. Neap. Syll. App. 5: 13 (1842) (Syn. M. racemosum (L.) Lam. & DC.)

Leaves narrow and often longer than the inflorescence, green, frequently tinged with purple, especially towards the base. Flowers very dark, or blackish-blue in a dense to loose raceme. Perianth oblong, strongly contracted at the mouth, with white teeth. Grassy places and light woodland and scrub. Widespread, occurring in most areas of Turkey (and in Europe and North Africa, east to Iran and Russia).

M. elwesii Baker is probably a synonym. *M. macranthum* Freyn seems to be a large-flowered form of *M. neglectum*.

M. parviflorum Desf., Fl. Atl. 1: 309 (1798)

The only autumn-flowering species. Leaves very narrowly linear. Flowers pale blue in loose racemes. Perianth only slightly constricted and almost campanulate. Dry hillsides and in shady places, at low altitudes. Areas ?6, 7, 8 (and in most Mediterranean countries).

M. tenuiflorum Tausch in Flora 24: 234 (1841)

Very similar to *M. comosum* (see above) but with blackish 'teeth' to the flower. Grassy places. Areas 8, 13, 15, 16, 17, 18 (and S.E. Europe).

M. trojana Heldr., from W. Turkey, is a poorly known taxon, described as having subsessile sterile flowers but is otherwise very similar in appearance to *M. tenuiflorum*.

M. weissii Freyn in Österr. Bot. Zeitschr. 28: 87 (1878)

This is similar in general appearance to *M. comosum* (see above) but the perianth 'teeth' are bright yellow. Rocky places. ? Areas 7, 8 (and in Crete and Cyclades).

12 *Nectaroscordum*

A small genus of only two or three species, closely related to *Allium* and possessing a similar onion or garlic smell when crushed or bruised. The very robust habit and umbels of large pendulous campanulate greenish flowers make it very distinctive. The perianth segments have three to five veins along the centre of each, whereas those of *Allium* species have only a single vein.

The one Turkish species is a useful plant for the semi-natural garden where it can seed around among other perennials and shrubs. Athough the flowers are of a subdued colour the plant has a graceful appearance since they are bell-like and held on slender pendulous stalks.

N. bulgaricum Janka in Österr. Bot. Zeitschr. 23: 242 (1873) (Syn: N. dioscoridis (Sibth. & Smith) Zahar.)

Medium to tall plant, 50–150 cm in height. Leaves mostly basal, strongly keeled, up to 5 cm wide, the inner leaf sheathing the flower stem for about one third of its length. Flowers dull greenish-white tinged with pale pink, campanulate, pendulous, about 1.5 cm long in a loose umbel, each one on a long arching pedicel which becomes erect in fruit. April–June. Woods or scrub below 1,000 metres. Areas 1, 5, 6, 7.

N. siculum (Ucria) Lindley has darker, greenish-red flowers and occurs in the western Mediterranean region, not in Turkey.

13 *Ornithogalum* (English: Star of Bethlehem; Turkish: Akyıldız)

A large genus of bulbous plants, especially common in the Mediterranean region and South Africa. Nearly all the Turkish species have starry flowers which are white, usually with a green stripe on the outside of each perianth segment.

Bulbs solitary or with many bulblets; leaves basal, linear to lanceolate or lorate, sometimes oblanceolate. Inflorescence a raceme, sometimes corymb-like if the lower pedicels are much longer than the upper. Stem leafless. Flowers usually white; tepals six, free, green-striped on the outside; stamens six. Fruit a capsule with or without distinct wings on the angles. Seeds black, flattish, ovoid or subglobose.

The Star of Bethlehem, *O. umbellatum*, is sometimes rather invasive and is best used for naturalizing between shrubs. Some species are very dwarf, non-invasive, and ideal for the rock garden or alpine house, for example *O. balansae*, *O. fimbriatum* and *O. lanceolatum*. All have white starry flowers except for the pendulous *O. nutans*.

In Turkey there are about 25 species, but the genus is not well-known and a revision may reveal a rather different number of taxa. The genus can be conveniently divided into five Sections in Turkey, and they are as follows:

A *Beryllis*: Rather tall plants. Inflorescence an elongated raceme with the pedicels all more or less the same length (more than 10 mm) and becoming erect or arched upwards in fruit. (*O. narbonense* and allies.)

B *Myogalum*: Inflorescence a more or less one-sided raceme with the pedicels short and all nearly equal in length. Stamens with the filaments tricuspidate. (*O. nutans* and *O. boucheanum*.)

C *Caruelia*: Tall plants with the inflorescence corymb-like, the lower pedicels being much longer than the upper. Flowers large, entirely white with no green stripe. Ovary blackish. (*O. arabicum* and *O. persicum*.)

D *Leptotesta*: Leaves becoming wider towards the apex, usually two per bulb. Inflorescence a short, few-flowered raceme with short pedicels which are deflexed in fruit. (*O. balansae* and allies.)

E *Heliocharmos*: Inflorescence corymb-like with the lower pedicels much longer than the upper. Leaves more than two, parallel-sided or tapering from base to apex (widest at base) with or without a white stripe on the upper surface. Flowers green-striped on the outside. (The majority of species.)

Since the distributions of the following species are not well-known the areas of occurrence in Turkey are tentative suggestions only.

Section A. *Beryllis*

O. narbonense L., Cent. Pl. 2: 15 (1756). (Syn. O. brachystachys K. Koch)
A tall species 30–100 cm in height. Leaves three to five, linear, about 1–1.5 cm wide, grey-green. Flowers starry, 1.5–2.5 cm diameter, up to 50 in a long

slender raceme, white with a narrow green stripe on the outside of each segment or unstriped; pedicels 1–3 cm long, erect in the fruiting state. April–July. Fields and rocky places. Widespread in Turkey (and S. Europe and W. Asia, from Spain east to Iran).

O. *arcuatum* Velen. is very similar but is a stouter plant and has longer pedicels which are strongly arched upwards in the fruiting stage. Areas 13, 14, 15, 16 (and in Iran and Iraq).

O. *kurdicum* Bornm. is similar to O. *arcuatum* in having arching pedicels but they are less than 1.5 cm long and the leaves are rather wider, sometimes as much as 2 cm broad. Possibly not occurring in Turkey.

O. *sphaerocarpum* Kerner in *Österr. Bot. Zeitschr.* 28: 15 (1878)

Plant 30–100 cm tall with five to eight linear, green leaves about 0.5–1 cm wide. Flowers about 1.5 cm diameter, pale greenish-white, usually about 15 to 30 in a long slender raceme; tepals only 2–3 mm wide and inrolled at the margins so that they appear even narrower; pedicels 1–2 cm long, erect in fruit. May–June. Scrub and light woodland. ? Areas 1, 2, 3, 5, 6, 9, 11, 12, 13 (and in S. Europe).

O. *pyrenaicum* L. is also found in Turkey. It is very similar to O. *sphaerocarpum* but has yellowish flowers, up to 40 in the raceme. Areas 3, 5, 6, 7, 11, 13 (and widespread in Europe).

Section B. *Myogalum*

O. *nutans* L., *Sp. Pl.*: 308 (1753)

Plant 15–35 cm tall. Leaves four to six, green, linear, about 1–1.5 cm wide. Flowers usually five to ten, white or silvery with a broad green stripe on the outside of each segment, rather bell-shaped and carried on short stalks in a dense, more or less one-sided raceme. Capsules fleshy and pendulous. March–May. Scrub and woods. Areas 1, 5, 6, 7 (and in S.E. Europe).

O. *boucheanum* Asch. is nearly identical but can be distinguished by the filaments of the three inner stamens having a tooth near the apex of the mid-vein. Possibly represented in Turkey in Area 1.

Section C. *Caruelia*

O. *arabicum* L., *Sp. Pl.*: 308 (1753)

Tall plant, usually 35–75 cm in height. Leaves about six to eight in a basal rosette, long-tapering at the apex and about 1–3 cm wide at the base. Flowers creamy-white, large and saucer-shaped, about 3–4 cm diameter, produced in a corymb-like raceme. Ovary blackish. April–May. Rocky places. Probably not native in Turkey but occurring sometimes as a relic of cultivation. Its natural distribution is unknown but it now occurs in many Mediterranean countries.

O. *persicum* Hausskn. ex Bornm. in *Beih. Bot. Centr.* 24, 2: 102 (1909)

This is similar in general appearance to O. *arabicum* but has more numerous smaller flowers in a dense, rather more conical, raceme. Areas 13, 18 (and in Iran).

Section D. *Leptotesta*

O. balansae Boiss., *Fl. Or.* 5: 222 (1884)

Only 3–6 cm tall. Leaves two, up to 1.5 cm wide, widening towards the apex, often bright glossy green. Flowers white with a very broad green stripe on the outside of the segments, rather erect, produced in a few-flowered raceme, sometimes solitary. May. Alpine meadows near melting snow. Areas ?3, 4, ?14, ?15, ?16 (and in the Caucasus).

O. brevipedicellatum Boiss. ex Baker in *Jour. Linn. Soc.* 13: 263 (1873)

About 10–30 cm tall. Leaves 4–7 mm wide, slightly wider at apex. Flowers rather transparent-white, with a narrow green stripe on the outside of the segments, produced on short pedicels in a dense raceme which is fastigiate in appearance; segments long-pointed at the apex; bracts large and papery. April–June. Rocky slopes. Areas 7, 13 (and in Iran).

O. oligophyllum Clarke, *Travels* 2, 3: 555 (1816)

A low plant, usually 7–15 cm tall. Leaves usually two, grey-green, 3–15 mm wide, oblanceolate with an abruptly narrowed apex. Flowers two to seven, white with a broad green stripe on each segment, produced in a short raceme; pedicels erect in flower, reflexed in fruit. April–June. Rocky and grassy places in the mountains, sometimes in sparse woodland. Areas ?1, ?2, 3, 5, ?6 (and in Greece).

These three species may be variants of just one, the oldest and therefore correct name for which would be *O. oligophyllum*.

Section E. *Heliocharmos*

O. armeniacum Baker, *Gard. Chron.* Ser. 2, 11: 748 (1879)

About 5–15 cm in height. Stem pubescent. Leaves white-striped above, filiform, only 1–2 mm wide, ciliate or pubescent. Flowers about 5–10, white with a green stripe on the outside of the segments, produced in a wide, rather flat-topped raceme; pedicels more or less horizontal in fruit. February–April. Dryish grassy places. Areas 2, 3, 4, 5, 6, 7, 8, 9, 11 (and in Balkans).

This differs from *O. fimbriatum*, which also has hairy leaves, in its narrow leaves and horizontal pedicels.

O. fimbriatum Willd. in *Ges. Naturf. Freunde Berlin Neue Schr.* 3: 420 (1801)

Usually 5–15 cm tall. Leaves 3–5 mm wide, often coiled on the ground, greyish, covered with silvery, often deflexed, hairs; upper surface not white-striped. Flowers three to ten, white with a green stripe on the outside of the segments, carried in a wide, flat-topped raceme; pedicels semi-erect at flowering time, sharply deflexed in fruit. April–May. Rocky or dry grassy places. Areas 1, 2, 5, 6 (and S.E. Europe).

This differs from *O. armeniacum* in having wider leaves and sharply deflexed fruiting pedicels.

O. lanceolatum Labill., *Ic. Pl. Syr.* 5: 11 (1812)

A dwarf plant with a compact rosette-like habit. Leaves 2 cm or more wide at the base, glossy green, lanceolate with a long-tapering apex. Flowers produced in a near-stemless raceme, giving a head-like appearance in the centre of the rosette; segments white with a green stripe on the outside; pedicels semi-erect. April–June. Wet mountain meadows. Areas 6, 7, 8, 10 (and in Syria and Lebanon).

The wider leaves in a flat rosette, and the near-stemless flower head, distinguish this from *O. montanum*.

O. montanum Cirillo in Ten., *Fl. Nap.* 1: 176 (1811)

Usually about 10–25 cm tall. Leaves three to six, green and unstriped, generally 1–2 cm wide at the base and long-tapering to an acute apex, produced in a rosette on the ground. Flowers about five to 15, white with a broad green stripe on the outside of the segments, carried in a wide often rather flat-topped raceme; pedicels horizontal or semi-erect in fruit. April–June. Grassy and rocky places or in damp mountain grassland. Areas 1, 5, 6, 7, 8 (and in S. Europe).

The narrower leaves and taller habit distinguish this from *O. lanceolatum*.

O. platyphyllum Boiss. (Syn. *O. tempskyanum* Freyn & Sint., ?*O. graciliflorum* K. Koch) is similar to *O. montanum* but has erect leaves. Areas 3, 4, 8, 9, 11, 12, 13, 14, 15, 16 (and in Iran and USSR).

O. orthophyllum Ten., *Fl. Nap.* 4, Syll. App. 3: 4 (1830). (Syn. *O. tenuifolium auct., non Guss.*)

Plant 5–30 cm in height. Leaves white-striped above, about 2–5 mm wide, glabrous. Flowers white with a green stripe on the outside of the segments, produced in a wide, rather flat-topped raceme; segments up to 2 cm long; pedicels semi-erect or horizontal in fruit, 2–3.5 cm long. April–May. Dry grassy places. Areas 1, 2, 3, 4, 5, 6, 7, 8, 9, 11, 14, 16 (and in S. Europe, Iran and Caucasus).

O. orthophyllum differs from *O. sibthorpii* and related species in not having sharply deflexed pedicels.

O. nivale Boiss., from Area 6, is very similar to *O. orthophyllum* but is very short with the fewer flowers carried only just above ground level; the perianth segments are only 1–1.2 cm long.

O. alpigenum Stapf has smaller perianth segments (0.8–1 cm long) than *O. orthophyllum* and fewer flowers which are carried in an oval raceme, not markedly flat-topped, and the pedicels are rather more erect. April–July. Grassy places and scrub. Areas 5, 6, 7, 8, 12.

O. umbellatum L. differs from *O. orthophyllum* in having longer pedicels (5–9 cm long in the fruiting stage). The bulb produces many bulblets, each of which has a single narrow leaf thus forming leafy clumps at flowering time; *O. orthophyllum* does not have clusters of bulblets. Woods and grassy places. Areas 1, 2, 5, 6, 7, 8, 13 (and widespread in Europe). *O. divergens* Boreau is very similar to *O. umbellatum* but has its bulb surrounded by non-leafy bulbets at flowering time, and it has reflexing pedicels. It has a similar distribution.

O. wiedemannii Boiss. is rather like *O. orthophyllum* at flowering time but the pedicels become spreading or recurved (but not sharply deflexed) in fruit. It differs from all other similar species in having a capsule with six distinct wings. In woods. Areas 1, 3, 9 (and in Greece).

O. byzantinum Azn., from the Istanbul area, is probably a synonym of *O.*

orthophyllum, as are *O. transcaucasicum* Miscz. and *O. woronowii* H. Kraschen from N.E. Turkey and Caucasus.

O. sibthorpii Greuter in *Boissiera* 13: 160 (1967). (Syn. *O. nanum* Sibth. & Smith, *C. sigmoideum* Freyn & Sint.)

Dwarf plant, only 5–10 cm tall. Leaves 1–4 mm wide with a white stripe on the upper surface. Flowers white with a rather pale green stripe on the outside of the segments, produced in a nearly stemless flat-topped raceme; pedicels sharply deflexed in the fruiting stage and then up to 2.5 cm long. March–May. Dry grassy places. Areas 1, 2, 3, 4, 5, 9 (and in S.E. Europe).

This differs from *O. orthophyllum* and related species by having sharply deflexed pedicels in the fruiting stage.

O. refractum Willd. is rather similar to *O. sibthorpii* but has many dormant bulblets around the parent bulb, and has longer fruiting pedicels, usually at least 3 cm long, and sometimes up to 5 cm April–June. Dry grassy or stony places. Areas 1, 5, 6 (and in S.E. Europe).

O. ulophyllum Hand.-Mazz. in *Ann. Naturk. Mus. Wien* 28: 19 (1914)

Usually 5–15 cm tall. Bulb long and slender, rather bottle-shaped. Leaves about 5–10 mm wide, with no white stripe, grey-green, lanceolate, ciliate, and pubescent on the upper surface, often undulate or twisted and reddish-margined. Flowers white with a green stripe on the outside of the segments, produced in a dense wide raceme, rather stiffly erect in appearance, especially at fruiting time. Rocky slopes. Areas 2, 6, 8, 9, 17 (and in Iraq).

O. comosum L. is not unlike this but is often taller, to 30 cm, and has much narrower leaves (2–4 mm) which do not have reddish margins. The pedicels are not as stiffly erect as in *O. ulophyllum*. Dryish grassy places. Areas 1, 2, 5, 6, 7, 10 (and in S. Europe).

14 *Puschkinia* (English: Lebanon Squill)

Small Scilla-like bulbous plants. Leaves usually two, linear or oblanceolate. Perianth pale blue, whitish or rarely greenish, campanulate. Segments six, joined into a short tube. Stamens six. Style with a capitate stigma. Fruit a many-seeded, three-valved capsule. There is a small, toothed cup surrounding the style and stamens and in this way it differs from *Scilla* and *Chionodoxa* which have no such corona.

A genus of one, possibly two, species in W. Asia.

This is an attractive spring-flowering bulb for the rock garden, alpine house or the front of a border. The flowers are normally pale blue but in gardens a white form is also known. *Puschkinia* is easily cultivated in well-drained soils which are however not too hot and dry.

P. scilloides Adams in *Nova Acta Acad. Sci. Petrop.* 14: 164 (1805). (Syn. *P. hyacinthoides* Baker, *P. libanotica* Zucc.)

Usually about 7–15 cm (rarely to 30 cm tall). Leaves two (to three), glossy green, 5–15 mm wide, linear-oblanceolate. Flowers one to ten, about 1–1.5 cm diameter, in a more or less one-sided raceme, campanulate, the tube 4–5 mm long. Segments spreading, pale blue or whitish with a darker blue stripe along the centre. Flowering April–June. Mountain meadows, usually near the snowline, 1,900–3,700 metres. Areas 13, 14, 15, 16 (and in Iraq, Lebanon, Syria, Iran and Caucasus).

In Hakkâri there is a variant with rather greenish flowers which may be a distinct species.

P. scilloides is a very ornamental and popular garden plant.

15 *Scilla* (English: Squill; Turkish: Yıldız-sümbülü)

A genus of about 40 species, mainly in Europe, Asia and South Africa. Many of the African species formerly in *Scilla* have been removed to the genus *Ledebouria*.

The genus is well known in gardens for the blue spring flowers, and the Turkish species are especially valuable for decorative purposes.

Bulbs covered by thin dark, sometimes purple, tunics. Leaves all basal, narrowly linear, strap-shaped or oblanceolate. Flowers few-to-many in the raceme, rarely solitary. Perianth with six free segments, flat and starry or bell-shaped, usually blue but sometimes violet or purple. Stamens six. Style undivided. Fruit a few-seeded three-valved capsule; seeds black, globose to ellipsoid.

In Turkey there are about ten species, although some recent work by Dr F. Speta, especially in dividing up *S. bifolia* and *S. siberica* into several species, increases this number. All the Turkish species flower in early-late spring, except for *S. autumnalis* (August–October).

Of the Turkish species, the brilliant blue forms of *S. siberica* are the most ornamental and ideally suited for the rock garden or in borders for an early spring display. *S. bithynica* is ideal for naturalizing in shrub borders and the beautiful but rare *S. rosenii* is best in a cool peat garden.

S. autumnalis L., Sp. Pl. 309 (1753)

Usually 5–15 cm in height. Leaves five to ten per bulb, absent or just visible at flowering time, very narrowly linear or filiform. Racemes about five to 20-flowered, the flowers 4–6 mm diameter, flat and starry, lilac-blue to violet, carried on slender pedicels. Often not far from the sea in sandy, rocky or grassy places or in open woods. Areas 1, 2, 3, 4, 5, 6, 7, 8 (and widespread in Europe, N. Africa and W. Asia).

S. bifolia L., Sp. Pl.: 309 (1753). (Syn. S. dubia K. Koch, S. minor K. Koch, S. xanthandra K. Koch and including S. nivalis Boiss. and S. uluensis Speta)

Plant 5–20 cm in height. Leaves usually two, broadly linear or oblanceolate, 3–10 mm wide. Flowers one to eight, starry, about 8–16 mm diameter, deep blue-violet to lilac, carried more or less erect in a one-sided raceme. Mountain meadows or woods, often not far from melting snow. Areas 1, 2, 3, 6, 7, 8, 9, 10, 11 (and widespread in C., E. and S. Europe).

S. bifolia is an extremely variable species in size of flower and stature. Several varieties have been named including var. *taurica* (var. *grandiflora*) which has many deep blue flowers, var. *whittallii*, described as having large flowers with a distinct white eye and var. *robusta* with a large inflorescence and broad leaves. In S.W. Turkey a variant occurs with more than two leaves, sometimes as many as five; this has been described as *S. bifolia* var. *polyphylla* (Syn. *S. longistylosa* Speta).

S. decidua Speta and *S. resselii* Speta, both described from Area 2, look very similar to *S. bifolia*.

S. bithynica Boiss., Diagn. Pl. Or. Nov. Ser. 1, 7: 111 (1846)

About 10–25 cm in height. Leaves about three per bulb, strap-like, 1–2.5 cm broad. Flowers usually six to 12, flattish and starry, mid-blue, about 1.5 cm diameter, produced in a fairly dense raceme. Water meadows and damp woods at low altitudes. Areas 1, 2, 5 (and in Bulgaria).

The long-cultivated *S. amoena* L., which is of unknown origin, has been recorded by Dr F. Speta as occurring in Area 2. The Kew specimen on which this record is based (Sintenis 4056) appears however to represent *S. bithynica*.

S. cilicica Siehe in Gard. Chron. 44: 194 (1908)

About 15–25 cm in height. Leaves three to four, developing in autumn and beginning to die back at the tips by flowering time, strap-like, 8–15 mm wide. Flowers five to 15 on short pedicels, 1–1.5 cm diameter, pale to mid-blue, campanulate at first but the segments soon reflexing, leaving the stamens protruding. Shady, rocky places. Areas 8, ?17 (and in Syria, Cyprus, Lebanon and Israel).

This differs from *S. siberica* and its relatives by producing its leaves in the autumn, long before flowering time in spring.

S. hyacinthoides L., Syst. Nat. ed. 12, 2: 243 (1767)

Bulb very large, up to 8 cm diameter. Height 1–1.5 metres in flower. Leaves eight to 12, strap-like or narrowly elliptical, 2–3 cm wide. Flowers numerous, up to 150 in a long raceme, flat and starry, mid-blue or violet, about 1 cm diameter, carried on very slender pedicels up to 3 cm long. Edges of fields, rocky place. Areas 6, 7, 8, 13, ?17, ?18 (and widespread throughout the Mediterranean region).

S. melaina Speta in Naturk. Jahrb. Stadt Linz 22: 67 (1976)

Plant 10–15 cm in height. Leaves three to four, strap-like, about 8–12 mm wide, well-developed and usually equalling the flowers. Flowers mid-blue, several in a loose raceme, bell-shaped at first opening almost flat and 1–2 cm diameter. In mountain scrub. Area 8 (? endemic).

Unlike *S. cilicica* this species produces its leaves in spring.

S. mesopotamica Speta, described from Area 17, is very similar to *S. melaina*.

S. ingridae Speta is also closely related but is smaller in all its parts with pale blue flowers; it was described from Area 8.

S. persica Haussk. in Mitt. Thür. Bot. Ver. n.s. 10: 44 (1897)

Plant 20–30 cm in height. Leaves five to seven, erect and bright shiny green, 1–1.5 cm broad. Flowers many, in long loose racemes, flat and starry, about

0.8–1.2 cm diameter, mid-blue, carried on horizontal pedicels 2–4 cm long. Water meadows. Area 13, ?16 (and in N. Iraq and W. Iran).

S. rosenii K. Koch in Linnaea 22: 250 (1849)

About 10–15 cm in height. Leaves usually two to three, broadly linear-oblanceolate, 1–2 cm wide. Flowers solitary, very large with perianth segments about 3 cm long and sharply reflexed, pale blue with a large white zone in the centre. Mountain meadows, near snow. Area 14, recorded near Kars (and in adjacent USSR).

S. siberica Haw. in Andrews, Bot. Reposit. 6, t. 365 (1804)
subsp. siberica

Plant 8–15 cm in height. Leaves usually two to three, broadly linear-oblanceolate, 1–2 cm wide. Flowers usually one to three, bell-shaped, pendulous, about 1–1.5 cm diameter, intense blue. Mountain meadows and scrub, often near snow. Subsp. *siberica* occurs mainly in the Caucasus and N.W. Iran but might be found in extreme N.E. Turkey.

Subsp. *armena* (Grossh.) Mordak (Syn. *S. armena* Grossh.) has solitary large tubby flowers which are usually pale blue with a dark blue stripe along the centre of each perianth segment. Mountain meadows near snow. Areas 4, 14 (and in S. Caucasus).

S. siberica is a variable plant and it is probable that *S. monanthos* K. Koch is a form of it; it has solitary smallish flowers of mid-blue.

S. leepii Speta, described from Area 13, is a similar solitary-flowered plant.

S. winogradowii Sosn. is like a robust *S. siberica* with several large pendulous deep blue flowers; it has been recorded from Area 4 (and adjacent USSR).

16 Tulipa (English: Tulip; Turkish: Lâle)

Tulips are very familiar plants with large upright showy flowers in late spring. There are a large number of species in Central Asia and the hybrids of these are well-known garden plants and have been for many centuries. The main centre of distribution is in Iran, Afghanistan and Russia, east of the Caspian. They are also common in the mountains of Turkey and are native in Europe, mainly in the south east. In Turkey there are about 14 species and these are mostly extremely variable.

It is fairly logical to assume that the great authors Dioscorides, Theophrastus and Pliny did not know of the existence of the tulip since it is not mentioned in their writings and it is unlikely that they would have ignored such a striking plant. In fact it seems quite probable that there are no, or very few, native *Tulipa* species in Europe since great surprise was registered in European gardening circles when the plant was introduced from the East.

In western Asia, tulips have been popular for a very long time and are mentioned before 1200 by the poet Omar Khayam. Seljuk artists adopted the flower as their motif in the twelfth century and they appear, under the name *Lâle*, in the writings of Mevlana Celaleddin Rûmi (1207–1273).

The European history of the garden tulip apparently dates from the middle of the sixteenth century when the Flemish diplomat Ogier Ghislain de Busbecq was sent by Ferdinand I of Austria to Istanbul, as Ambassador to Süleyman the Magnificent. Marvelling at the many flowers, such as Narcissus and Hyacinths, Busbecq further relates that he saw in the gardens of Adrianople an unknown flower, in gorgeous colours, which the Turks called *Tulipam*. This letter, the *Epistolae de rebus turcicis*, written in 1554, constitutes as far as is known the first mention of the tulip in Europe. The word *Tulipam* is probably a mistake by Busbecq, since *Lâle* is the accepted Turkish (and Persian) word for the plant.

In May 1673 the Frenchman Antoine Calland (see Schefer[119]) travelled by the same route as Busbecq from Istanbul to Edirne and also recorded that there were fields of cultivated tulips; these are no longer in existence.

It is generally accepted that Busbecq was the first to introduce tulips to Europe and that several of the species which occur apparently wild are in fact escapes from cultivation.

Short-to-medium bulbous plants; the bulbs, which are sometimes stoloniferous, are covered with thin or leathery brown or black tunics which are either glabrous or lined with hairs on the inside. Stems carry alternate leaves, sometimes only two but usually several. Flowers erect, usually solitary but sometimes up to four, either bowl-shaped with a rounded base or funnel-shaped with a tapered base. Perianth segments six, free to the base, often with a coloured blotch at the base. Stamens six, filaments with or without a tuft of hairs in the basal part. Stigma sessile on the ovary, or with a short style. Fruit an erect capsule, oblong to nearly globose, sometimes with a beak-like apex; seeds many, flat.

The most important features used in distinguishing the species are (1) the type of bulb tunic hairs, (2) the absence or presence of hairs at the base of the filaments, (3) the colour of the flowers and central blotch, if any, (4) the shape of the flower, and, (5) to a lesser extent, the colour and number of the leaves.

In the genus *Tulipa* two main Sections are recognized, the Leiostemones and the Eriostemones. In order to assist in identification, we have arranged the 14 Turkish species in these two Sections and have further subdivided each of these into three informal groups, A, B and C, on the basis of flower colour.

Most of the wild Turkish species are showy and worthy of a place in gardens but they are not always easy to grow outside in cool climates since the bulbs require a warm dry period in summer. In such areas they are best grown in a bulb frame or alpine house.

Flower diameter is a difficult measurement, but is of use in recognition and the following guide is given. The flower is measured across its width when it is young and fully open in sunshine – in some species this might be flat and starry, in others bowl-shaped or funnel-shaped. 'Small flowers' means those 1.5–3.5 cm in diameter; 'medium-sized flowers' include those 4–5.5 cm in diameter; and 'large flowers' refer to those 6–8 cm in diameter.

The epithets *turcarum* and *turcica* have been used several times by botanists for Turkish tulips, understandably causing some confusion. These names can be interpreted as follows:

T. turcarum Gesner is a synonym of *T. armena* Boiss.

T. turcica Griseb. is a synonym of *T. orphanidea* Boiss. ex Heldr.

T. turcica Kunth is a synonym of *T. acuminata* Vahl ex Hornem.

T. turcica Roth is a synonym of *T. sylvestris* L.

Section 1. *Leiostemones*

Filaments glabrous at the base; flowers bowl-shaped or cup-shaped with a rounded base (except *T. sprengeri*) and with no obvious waist above the base.

A Flowers white inside with small purple central blotch, red outside

T. clusiana DC. in Redouté, *Liliacées* 1, t. 37 (1802)

Bulb with long hairs protruding from the apex. Leaves grey-green. Flowers one to two, medium-sized, white with a small dark purple blotch inside, pinkish-crimson edged with white on the outside of the outer segments. April–May. In or near cultivation. Not native in Turkey but occasionally cultivated. In S. Europe and the Aegean Is. it is naturalized. (Native of Iran, Afghanistan and Pakistan.)

B Flowers orange-red with no dark central blotch; flowers not rounded at the base

T. sprengeri Baker in *Gard. Chron.* 1894: 716 (1894). (Syn. *T. brachyanthera* Freyn)

Bulb tunic thin and papery, glabrous or with a few hairs only on the inside. Leaves five to six, bright shiny green. Flowers one to two, medium-sized, orange-red, yellowish on the outside, with no blotch in the centre. May–June, the latest species of Tulip to flower. Area 3 (endemic). This has probably been collected only once, in the region of Amasya. It is cultivated in Europe to some extent and is very successful, seeding and flowering freely in some British gardens. The original collection was of living material and almost certainly all the currently cultivated plants are derived from this, for it has not been rediscovered in the wild.

C Flowers red, usually with a dark blotch, or rarely yellow with or without a blotch; flower rounded at the base

T. agenensis DC. in Redouté, *Liliacées*, t. 60 (1804). (Syn. *T. oculis-solis* St.-Amans)

Bulb tunic densely lined with hairs inside. Leaves green. Flowers solitary, large, bright red, paler or even yellowish on the outside; basal blotch on each segment often long, narrow and pointed, blackish edged with yellow; perianth segments more than three times as long as wide. April. Usually in cultivated land. Areas 1, 3, 5, 6, 8 (and in S. France and Greek Is.). Probably a native of C. Asia.

T. aleppensis Boiss. ex Regel in *Acta Horti Petrop.* 2: 450 (1873)

Bulb tunic densely lined with long hairs. Leaves grey-green. Flowers solitary, large, red with a paler inside; basal blotch on each segment rather short and not markedly pointed, blackish, usually not edged with yellow. March–May. Usually in cultivated land. Areas 13, 17, 18 (and in Syria).

T. armena Boiss., Diagn. Pl. Or. Nov. Ser. 2, 4: 99 (1859). (Syn. T. willmottae Freyn, T. mucronata Fomin, T. suaveolens Roth, T. turcarum Gesner)

Bulb tunic lined with a thin layer of long hairs or with short hairs at the base and apex only. Leaves grey-green, often very undulate at the margin. Flowers usually solitary, medium-sized, bright red or crimson-red, often pale or yellowish outside; basal blotch blackish, rather small. April–June. Stony slopes in mountains, about 1,000–3,000 metres. Areas 3, 4, 6, 7, 8, 10, 11, 12, 13, 14, 16 (and in N.W. Iran and S. Caucasus).

T. mucronata Fomin is a robust yellow-flowered form of T. armena with non-wavy leaves.

T. galatica Freyn is apparently a yellow-flowered form of T. armena which has no blotch at the base of the segments. It was collected near Amasya.

T. lutea Freyn is another yellow-flowered mutant with a bluish blotch in the centre of the flower. It was also collected in the vicinity of Amasya.

The variant of T. armena which has only short hairs on the bulb tunic is distributed mainly in the central and southern part of the range. It was described as T. oculis-solis var. lycica Baker, but is to be recognized as a variant of T. armena by W. Marais in the Flora of Turkey account of the genus. This has several synonyms, namely T. ciliatula Bak., T. concinna Bak., T. foliosa Stapf and T. heterochroa Freyn.

T. julia K. Koch in Linnaea 22: 225 (1849). (Syn. 'T. montana' of various authors but not of Lindley; T. kaghyzmanica Fomin)

Bulb tunic densely lined with hairs. Leaves grey-green. Flowers usually solitary, small to medium, bright red or orange-red or yellow, with a rather small black basal blotch which is often edged with yellow; the yellow form retains the black blotch. May. Rocky hillsides, about 1,500–2,500 metres. Areas 13, 14, 15, 16 (and in N.W. Iran and Transcaucasus). In some populations red and yellow forms occur, together with some intermediate ones striped red and yellow; it is one of these striped forms which was described as T. kaghyzmanica.

T. julia is very similar to T. armena but T. armena has, on the whole, larger flowers. The bulb tunics differ and provide a means of distinguishing between the two. In T. julia the tunics are lined with a thick felt-like layer of hairs while in T. armena the tunics are either only hairy at the base and apex or have long hairs which do not form a dense mat.

T. praecox Ten., Fl. Nap. 1: 170 (1811)

This is like T. agenensis in having densely hairy bulb tunics and very large red flowers but the segments are only about twice as long as wide and have a comparatively small black basal blotch, edged with yellow (not a long narrow blotch as is usual in T. agenensis). April–May. Rocky slopes and cultivated land. Areas ?3, 5, 6 (and in S. Europe, but probably naturalized).

T. sintenisii Baker in Gard. Chron. 1891: 330 (1891)

Bulb producing stolons; tunic hairs only at the base and apex. Leaves grey-green. Flowers usually solitary, medium-sized, orange-red, often paler on the outside; central blotch rather small, blackish or very dark green, usually without a yellow margin; outer perianth segments longer than the inner ones; the greenish pollen is distinctive. April–June. Usually in cultivated land. Areas 4, 8, ?11, 12, 13, 14, 15, 16, 17 (probably not native but country of origin unknown.)

T. undulatifolia **Boiss.,** ***Diagn. Pl. Or. Nov.*** **Ser. 1, 5: 57 (1844). (Syn.** ***T. boeotica*** **Boiss. & Heldr.,** ***T. eichleri*** **Regel)**
Bulb tunics papery with a few hairs inside. Leaves grey-green, usually with very undulate margins, the upper ones finely pubescent. Flowers usually solitary, medium to large, orange-red or brilliant deep red, paler on the outside; blotch acute to obtuse, blackish, usually surrounded by a yellow zone. April–May. Cultivated land. Areas 1, 5, 6, 9, 10 (and in the Balkans and S. Caucasus).

Section 2. *Eriostemones*

Filaments hairy on the basal part; flowers funnel-shaped with a tapered base and/or a constriction or waist above the base in the bud or young flower stage.

A Flowers white inside with a yellow centre

T. biflora **Pallas,** ***Reise*** **3: 727 (1776). (Syn.** ***T. polychroma*** **Stapf).**
Bulb tunic densely hairy inside. Leaves two only, dull grey-green. Flowers one to three, small, white inside with a yellow basal blotch, outside tinged with purple, green or grey. April–June. Rocky slopes in mountains, about 2,000–3,000 metres. Areas 15, ?16 (and in S.E. Russia, Transcaspia, Crimea, Jordan, Iraq, Iran, Egypt and Yugoslavia).

B Flowers yellow, red or orange inside, sometimes with a dark centre

T. orphanidea **Boiss. ex Heldr. in** ***Gartenfl.*** **11: 309 (1862). (Syn.:** ***T. bithynica*** **Griseb. ex Baker,** ***T. hageri*** **Heldr.** ***T. thracica*** **Davidoff,** ***T. hellespontica*** **Degen,** ***T. hayatii*** **O. Schwarz,** ***T. whittallii*** **A. D. Hall,** ***T. turcica*** **Griseb.)**
Bulb tunic with hairs at the base and apex only. Leaves grey-green to shiny green. Flowers usually one to three, small to medium-sized, dull red, orange-red or orange-yellow with a blackish or dark green blotch in the centre and often tinged greenish or yellowish on the exterior of the outer segments, very rarely wholly yellow with a reddish suffusion on the outside. In the yellow forms it can be distinguished from *T. sylvestris* by having brownish anthers (yellow in *T. sylvestris*). April–May. Rocky places, often in scrub, up to 2,000 metres. Areas 1, 5, 6, 7 (and in the Balkans).
    This is a very variable plant and some of the variants have been described as separate species. *T. hellespontica* was distinguished by its pubescent stem and ovary, *T. thracica* by the stem being pubescent only in the upper part and by the ovary being pubescent, and *T. hayatii* by its hairy stem and

glabrous ovary. The rest of the names given in the synonymy above applied to plants with glabrous stems. They were separated as species on the basis of flower colour (reddish or orange), on the colour of the basal blotch on the segments (dark green or blackish) and on flower size.

Hayek in *Prodr. Fl. Penins. Balcan.* 3: 69 (1933), using these characters, distinguished *T. bithynica*, *T. hageri* and *T. orphanidea* with glabrous stems and ovaries, from *T. thracica* with stems and ovaries pubescent.

W. Marais, however, in his treatment of the genus for the *Flora of Turkey*, considers that these features are unreliable and regards the above names as representing variants of the one species, *T. orphanidea*.

T. sylvestris L., *Sp. Pl.* 305 (1753). (Syn.: *T. australis* Link, *T. thirkeana* K. Koch, *T. celsiana* DC., *T. biebersteiniana* Schultes fil.)

Bulb tunic hairy at the base and apex only. Leaves grey-green. Flowers usually solitary, small, yellow with no dark blotch in the centre, usually tinged pinkish or reddish-purple on the outside. April–May. In woods, rocky or grassy places up to 3,000 metres. Areas ?1, 4, 5, 6, 7, 8, 9, 15 (and widespread in Europe, N. Africa, Iran and Russia). *Flora Europaea* recognizes two subspecies; the Turkish material is rather small-flowered and would represent subsp. *australis* (Link) Pamp. in the system of *Flora Europaea*.

T. tchitounyi Azn., collected in the region of Van, appears to be very similar to *T. sylvestris*. It was described as having an unscented very small nodding yellow flower.

C Flowers pink or purplish inside with a yellow, purple or blue blotch

T. humilis Herbert in *Bot. Reg.* 30, misc. 30 (1844). (Syn.: *T. pulchella* (Fenzl ex Regel) Baker, *T. violacea* (Boiss. & Buhse) Baker)

Bulb tunics with hairs at the base and apex only. Leaves grey-green. Flowers solitary, small, pinkish, purplish or lilac with a yellow, dark purple or dark blue blotch at the centre. April–June. Rocky slopes or sparse alpine turf, often near the snow line, 1,000–3,500 metres. Areas 8, 10, 15, 16 (and in S. Caucasus and Iran).

T. saxatilis Sieber ex Sprengel, *Syst. Veg.* 2: 63 (1825)

Bulb often stoloniferous; tunic with hairs at the apex only. Leaves shiny green. Flowers usually one to three, medium-sized, pink or lilac-pink with a yellow centre. Rocky places, up to 500 metres. It occurs on Crete and Rhodes and was once collected by Whittall of Izmir, but this specimen is said to have been found on a neighbouring island.

T. saxatilis was until recently thought to be absent from the Turkish mainland, but on 21 March 1981 T. Baytop visited the Marmaris peninsula in S.W. Turkey and recorded the plant growing abundantly in two sites. Rocky places, area 6 (and in Crete and Rhodes).

17 *Urginea* (English: Sea Squill; Crusaders' Spears; Turkish: Adasoğanı)

Robust bulbous plants with large basal leaves, appearing after the flowers. Scape slender, much exceeding the leaves and carrying a long raceme of flowers. Perianth segments six, free, white. Stamens six, inserted at the base of the segments. Stigma capitate. Fruit a globose or oblong three-valved capsule containing many flattened seeds.

A genus of about 50 species in Africa and Asia. In Turkey only one species.

Although striking when seen flowering in its wild situations, the Sea Squill rarely performs well in gardens. Originating from low altitudes near the coast it is a very tender plant in northern climates and is not showy enough to merit greenhouse space, and its gross leaves are very space-consuming.

U. maritima (L.) Baker in *Jour. Linn. Soc.* 13: 221 (1873). (Syn. *Scilla maritima* L.)

Bulb up to 10 cm diameter, usually on the surface of the soil. Leaves not present at flowering time, produced during autumn and winter in a basal tuft, elliptic-lanceolate, about 4–8 cm wide, deep glossy green. Flower stem about 1–1.5 metres tall with a long raceme of white starry flowers, each with a brownish or purplish line along the centre and about 1–1.5 cm diameter. Flowering August–October. Rocky or sandy places at low altitudes, sometimes on the sea shore. Areas 6, 7, 8 (and widespread in the Mediterranean region).

EIGHT

Non-bulbous Liliaceae in Turkey

In addition to the 'bulbous' members of Liliaceae dealt with in this book, there are in Turkey many non-bulbous species. The following list is not complete and is provided only as an indication of the great range of plants involved in this very diverse family.

Aloe vera (L.) Burm. fil.
Anthericum liliago L.
Asparagus (Turkish name: *Kuşkonmaz*)
A. acutifolius L.
A. brevifolius Boiss.
A. officinalis L.
A. tenuifolius Lam.
A. verticillatus L.
Asphodeline anatolica E. Tuzlaci
A. baytopae E. Tuzlaci
A. brevicaulis (Bertol.) Gay ex Baker
A. cilicica E. Tuzlaci
A. damascena (Boiss.) Baker subsp. *damascena*
A. damascena (Boiss.) Baker subsp. *gigantea* E. Tuzlaci
A. damascena (Boiss.) Baker subsp. *ovoidea* E. Tuzlaci
A. damascena (Boiss.) Baker subsp. *rugosa* E. Tuzlaci
A. dendroides (Hoffm.) Woronow
A. globifera Gay
A. liburnica (Scop.) Reichb.
A. lutea (L.) Reichb.
A. peshmeniana E. Tuzlaci
A. prismatocarpa Gay
A. rigidifolia Boiss.
A. taurica (Pallas) Kunth
A. tenuior (Fischer) Ledeb. subsp. *tenuiflora* (K. Koch) E. Tuzlaci var. *tenuiflora*
A. tenuior (Fischer) Ledeb. subsp. *tenuiflora* (K. Koch) E. Tuzlaci var. *puberulenta* E. Tuzlaci
Asphodelus fistulosus L.
A. messeniacus Heldr.
A. microcarpus Viv.
Convallaria majalis L. (probably of cultivated origin, Turkish name: *Inci çiçeği*)

Danae racemosa (L.) Moench
Eremurus cappadocicus Gay
E. spectabilis M. Bieb. (Turkish name: *Çiriş*)
Narthecium ossifragum (L.) Hudson
N. caucasicum Miscz.
Paris incompleta M. Bieb.
Polygonatum (Turkish name: *Süleyman mühürü*)
P. cilicicum Schott ex Kotschy
P. glaberrimum K. Koch
P. latifolium (Jacq.) Desf.
P. multiflorum (L.) All.
P. orientale Desf.
P. verticillatum (L.) All.
Ruscus (Turkish name: *Tavşanmemesi*)
R. aculeatus L.
R. hypoglossum L. (Turkish name: *Yalova mercanı*)
R. hypophyllum L.
Smilax (Turkish name: *Gıcır, Özdikeni, Saparna*)
S. aspera L.
S. excelsa L.
Veratrum (Turkish name: *Çöpleme*)
V. album L.

NINE

Economic Importance of Turkish Bulbous Plants

Most of the bulbous plants in Turkey are known for their ornamental value, but a number of them also have some importance for culinary and pharmaceutical purposes. For example, some *Allium* species have been cultivated in Turkey for a very long time for their use as onion, garlic or leeks. In east Anatolia the leaves and bulbs of some wild *Allium* species are often used for flavouring, and one can mention in this respect *A. ampeloprasum* (Turkish: *yabani sarımsak*) in Tunceli, and *A. vineale* (Turkish: *sirmo*) in Van.

In central and east Anatolia the corms of *Crocus cancellatus, C. kotschyanus* and *C. biflorus* are often eaten raw or baked. Sometimes they are collected in such quantity that they are sold in bundles in the markets. The tubers of many Orchidaceae (mainly *Orchis* and *Ophrys*) are dried and powdered, then added to milk and heated to produce the drink *salep*.

Many bulbs were known for their medicinal value to the ancient Greeks and of these a considerable proportion are native to Turkey. Species which have been used in this way and occurring in Turkey include *Narcissus tazetta, Pancratium maritimum, Crocus sativus, Gladiolus communis, Iris germanica, Allium spp., Colchicum spp., Hyacinthus orientalis, Lilium candidum, Ornithogalum umbellatum, Urginea maritima*. The Saffron Crocus, *C. sativus*, is still cultivated near the town of Safranbolu (= 'full of saffron'.)

More recently, the bulbs of *Galanthus, Leucojum* and *Narcissus* have aroused interest because of their content of galanthamine, a substance found to be of use in the treatment of poliomyelitis.

From the pharmacological and chemical viewpoints, the bulbous plants of Turkey have not yet been thoroughly investigated. Just taking the genus *Colchicum* as an example, there are 30 species in Turkey but only one, *C. autummale*, has been studied in any depth and even here in the one species there is much more chemical work to be done.

Turkey exports bulbs, corms and tubers for horticultural purposes, mainly gathered from the wild in the Anatolian mountains. Regional collectors bring their material into Antalya, Izmir and Istanbul where it is handled by the exporting company. After grading and drying the bulbs are sent to wholesale dealers in other countries. The amount of material exported from Turkey has increased continuously each year: for example in 1950 the total weight of bulbs was 18,414 kg while in 1978 it had reached a staggering 297,437 kg. The yearly average income Turkey gains from the export of these bulbs is about $1,000,000. The following table, provided by the Turkish State Institute of Statistics, shows the amount purchased by each importing country during the years 1975–1982.

Export Quantity (Kg)

Countries	1975	1976	1977	1978
Bulgaria	—	—	—	—
Denmark	941	—	975	1,632
Germany (W.)	77,351	50,634	28,315	7,796
Holland	125,235	142,463	149,798	184,506
Jordan	—	16,500	30,000	102,243
Kuwait	—	16,510	—	—
Lebanon	—	211,884	50,000	—
Norway	225	—	—	—
Sweden	—	—	—	—
Switzerland	8,615	4,196	4,001	—
Syria	—	29,970	10,000	—
United Kingdom	21,907	10,804	6,501	616
USA	4,865	1,180	4,304	644
Total	**239,138**	**484,141**	**288,894**	**297,437**

Countries	1979	1980	1981	1982
Bulgaria	—	—	—	21,000
Denmark	8,277	4,054	3,758	—
Germany (W.)	8,295	26,632	68,233	25,794
Holland	221,407	209,105	277,308	295,007
Jordan	84,980	79,695	169,230	—
Kuwait	—	—	—	—
Lebanon	4,750	—	—	—
Norway	—	—	—	—
Sweden	—	—	—	1,023
Switzerland	—	3,215	4,711	3,969
Syria	—	—	—	—
United Kingdom	9,794	11,630	19,293	19,493
USA	—	896	3,345	—
Total	**337,503**	**335,227**	**545,878**	**366,286**

Since the majority of these bulbs are taken from the wild, the Turkish government has recently limited the export to some extent in order to conserve the native flora. Although the cultivation of these bulbs has started in Turkey, at present the demand is too great to be supplied from horticultural material alone and the wild stocks continue to be depleted.

Today, Turkey exports bulbs, corms and tubers of the following species:

Amaryllidaceae

Galanthus elwesii Hook. fil.
G. latifolius Rupr.
Leucojum aestivum L.
Narcissus tazetta L.
Pancratium maritimum L.

Sternbergia clusiana Ker-Gawler
S. fischeriana (Herbert) Rupr.
S. lutea (L.) Ker-Gawler
S. sicula Tineo

Araceae

Arisarum vulgare Targ.-Tozz.
Arum albispathum Steven
A. dioscoridis Sibth. & Smith

A. italicum Miller
A. orientale M. Bieb.
Dracunculus vulgaris Schott

Geraniaceae

Geranium tuberosum L.

Iridaceae

Crocus ancyrensis Maw
C. biflorus Miller
C. cancellatus Herbert
C. flavus Weston
C. fleischeri Gay
C. kotschyanus K. Koch
C. pallasii Goldb.
C. pulchellus Herbert
C. sativus L.

C. speciosus M. Bieb.
Iris iberica subsp. *elegantissima* Sosn.
I. germanica L.
I paradoxa Steven
I. persica L.
I. reticulata M. Bieb.
I. sari Schott
I. tuberosa L. (*Hermodactylus*)

Liliaceae

Bellevalia ciliata Cirillo
Chionodoxa luciliae Boiss.
C. sardensis Barr & Sugden
C. tmoli Whittall
Colchicum speciosum Steven
C. variegatum L.
C. cilicicum Dammer
Fritillaria acmopetala Boiss.
F. imperialis L.
F. persica L.
F. pontica Wahlenb.

Lilium candidum L.
L. martagon L.
Muscari muscarimi Medicus (*M. moschatum* Willd.)
Ornithogalum nutans L.
Scilla bifolia L.
Tulipa hageri Heldr.
T. humilis Herbert
T. praecox Ten.
T. undulatifolia Boiss.
Urginea maritima (L.) Baker

Oxalidaceae

Oxalis cernua Thunb.

Primulaceae

Cyclamen cilicium Boiss. & Heldr.
C. coum Miller

C. persicum Miller

Ranunculaceae

Anemone
A. blanda Schott & Kotschy

A. coronaria L.
Eranthis cilicica Schott & Kotschy

TEN
Cultivation of Turkish Bulbous Plants

The majority of the bulbous species in Turkey grow on plateaux and mountains above 1,000 metres altitude. The climate of these areas is characterized by a hot dry summer and a cold snowy winter. The rain is confined to spring and autumn and these are the times when nearly all the bulbs flower. The spring species flower as the snow melts and they grow very rapidly so that by the time the soil has dried out for the summer months the fruits have been produced and the growth cycle for that season is completed. The bulbs then lie in an almost dormant state, many of them without any living roots, until the following autumn when growth is triggered off again by dampness and cooler temperatures.

On the higher mountain slopes these spring species experience very little autumn rain since the first precipitation on to the dry soil is often in the form of snow, and the plants maintain their dormancy until the melting of the snow in spring. In fact the bulbs are not truly dormant, for even in the case of a bulb or corm which has no roots in summer, the process of bud initiation is taking place inside the growing point.

The problems of cultivation in gardens at low altitudes, or in areas which have little snow, arise because the plants attempt to grow too early, sometimes in the autumn, and thus produce young leaves which are susceptible to frost and disease. For this reason, the best way of growing most of these bulbs is in a bulb frame or cold greenhouse where there is shelter from excess rain in autumn. In summer the bulbs can be dried off completely to allow ripening and bud initiation to take place.

The autumn-flowering bulbs in Anatolia usually flower in the period September to November as the temperature falls and humidity rises. These plants then go into a period of semi-dormancy below ground and are often buried in snow. In spring when the snow melts the leaves and fruits are pushed above ground where they mature rapidly before the onset of the hot dry summer. Obviously, the cultivation of these autumn species is similar to that of the spring ones, but in order to encourage flowering some water must be given in September and then no more until the spring.

Many of the Turkish bulbs occur in calcareous soils and some attention must be given to the type of soil used in cultivation. A knowledge of the habitat and soil type is most helpful when considering cultivation methods for a particular species. Drainage is most important and it is best to add some sharp sand or grit to the soil mixture to ensure that any excess water drains away quickly. Most of the soils in which the Anatolian bulbs occur naturally are rather low in humus content so that on the whole it is best to avoid adding much organic matter, which is rich in nitrogen, to potting compost.

Propagation of the bulbs depends very much upon the behaviour of the species concerned. Some species (such as Oncocyclus *Iris*) make clumps of rhizomes which can be divided, and *Fritillaria* species often produce many offset bulbs. However, plants which do not increase in this way may have to be propagated by seed, and it may take from three to ten years to produce flowering-sized bulbs.

ELEVEN

Some Selected Turkish Names

Allium	*Yabani soğan*
A. ampeloprasum	*Yabani sarımsak*
A. cepa	*Soğan*
A. hirsutum	*Körmen*
A. macrochaetum	*Kaya sarımsağı*
A. porrum	*Pırasa*
A. rotundum	*Körmen*
A. sativum	*Sarımsak*
A. vineale	*Sirmo*
A. zebdanense	*Geyik körmeni*
Colchicum	*Acıçiğdem*
Convallaria majalis	*İnciçiçeği*
Crocus	*Çiğdem*
C. sativus	*Safran*
Eremurus spectabilis	*Çiriş*
Fritillaria	*Terslâle*
F. imperialis	*Şahtuğu, Ağlayangelin*
F. latifolia	*Beneklilâle*
Gagea	*Altınyıldız*
Galanthus	*Kardelen, Aktaş*
Gladiolus	*Kargasoğanı, Kuzgunkılıcı*
Gynandriris	*Yumrulu süsen*
Hyacinthella	*Küçük sümbül*
Hyacinthus	*Sümbül*
Iris (Pogon)	*Süsen*
Iris (Apogon)	*Çayır süseni*
Iris (Oncocyclus)	*Sultan nevruzu*
Iris (Reticulata)	*Meşe nevruzu*
Iris (Juno)	*Nevruz, Navruz*
I. germanica	*Mor süsen*
I. orientalis	*Çayır süseni*
I. pseudacorus	*Bataklık süseni*
I. xanthospuria	*Sarı süsen*
Leucojum aestivum	*Akçabardak, Karçiçeği*
Lilium	*Zambak*
L. candidum	*Ak zambak*
L. martagon	*Kırmızı zambak*
Muscari	*Arapsümbülü*

M. comosum	*Dağsoğanı*
M. muscarimi	*Misksoğanı, Müşkülüm*
Narcissus	*Nergiz*
N. poeticus	*Zerrinkadeh*
Ornithogalum	*Akyıldız*
Pancratium maritimum	*Kumzambağı*
Scilla	*Yıldızsümbülü*
Tulipa	*Lâle*
T. clusiana	*Çelebi lâlesi*
T. hageri	*Geyik lâlesi*
T. humilis	*Çoban lâlesi*
T. praecox	*Kaba lâle*
T. saxatilis	*Taşlıca lâlesi*
T. sylvestris	*Kuşağzı*
Urginea maritima	*Adasoğanı*

TWELVE

Turkish Summary

Anadolu birçok yumrulu ve soğanlı bitkinin vatanıdır. Bu bölgenin soğanlı bitkileri hakkındaki ilk bilgiler, yaklaşık olarak İ.Ö.2000 yıllarında yazılmış olan, Hitit tabletlerinde bulunmaktadır. Bu tabletlerden Hititlerin soğan, sarımsak, pırasa ve safran gibi bitkileri tanıdıklarını öğreniyoruz. Hititler, Anadolu yaylalarında karların erimesi ve yumrulu bitkiler (*Crocus, Colchicum, Hyacinthus, Iris* gibi) in çiçeklenmesi ile gelen ilkbahar'ı "Bahar Bayramı" adı verilen törenler ile kutlamaktaydılar.

Anadolunun soğanlı bitkileri hakkında Strabon, Dioscorides, İbn Baytar gibi klasik devir yazarlarının eserlerinde de birçok bilgi bulunmaktadır. Mesela Anazarba (Adananın kuzeyinde) lı Dioscorides'in İ.S. birinci yüzyılda yazdığı eserinde *Allium cepa, A. porpum, A. sativum, A. scorodoprasum, Crocus sativus, Colchicum variegatum, Lilium candidum, Narcissus tazetta* gibi Anadoluda yetişen birçok soğanlı bitkinin özellikleri ve tedavi alanındaki kullanılışları hakkında etraflı bilgi bulunmaktadır.

İsviçreli botanik bilgini E. Boissier'nin abidevi eseri Flora Orientalis'in 1884 yılında yayınlanmış olan 5. cildinde, tetkik konumuz olan Amaryllidaceae, İridaceae ve Liliaceae familyalarına ait 220 türün Anadoluda yetiştiği kayıtlıdır. Kitabımızda ise bu familyalara ait 500 kadar türün ismi bulunmaktadır. Bu duruma göre, 5. cildin yayınlanmasından bu yana geçen 100 yıla yakın bir zaman içinde, Anadolunun soğanlı bitkileri hakkındaki bilgilerimizin % 100 oranından fazla bir artış gösterdiği anlaşılmaktadır. Bu yeni bilgileri Flora Orientalis'in yayınlanmasından sonra Anadoluda araştırma gezileri yapmış ve bitki kolleksiyonları hazırlamış olan F. W. Noe, P. Sintenis, J. V. Aznavour, J. J. Manissadjian, W. Siehe, K. Krause, K. Balls ile diğer araştırıcıların gayretlerine borçluyuz. Bu araştırıcıları okuyuculara tanıtmak gayesiyle kitabımıza bilhassa Türkiyenin soğanlı bitkileri ile ilgilenmiş araştırıcı ve toplayıcıların kısa biografilerini ve fotoğraflarını taşıyan bir bölüm ilâve etmeyi uygun bulduk.

Osmanlı imparatorluğu döneminde soğanlı bitkiler diğer süs bitkilerinden daha fazla bir öneme sahip olmuştur. Gül ve karanfil ayrı tutulur ise yüzyıllar boyu lâle (*Tulipa*), sümbül (*Hyacinthus*), zerren (*Narcissus*) ve süsen (*Iris*) türlerinin binlerce kültür formu İstanbul bahçelerinin başlıca süs bitkileri olmuştur.

Lâle 17. ve 18. yüzyıllarda İstanbulda büyük bir önem ve değer kazanmıştır. Bu çiçeğin esas vatanının Orta Asya olduğu tahmin edilmektedir. Anadoluda ise 20 kadar yabani lâle türünün yetişmekte olduğu bilinmektedir. Lâle'nin Avrupaya hangi yolla geçtiği tam olarak bilinmemekle beraber Orta Asyadan İrana, oradan da Anadolu ve Avrupaya geçtiği düşünülmektedir.

Lâle motifine 12. yüzyıldan itibaren Anadolu Selçuklarına ait eserlerde rastlanmaktadır. Bizanslılara ait yapılar, sanat eserleri ve paralarda lâle motifine rastlanmaması, Türklerden önce İstanbulda lâlenin bir değerinin bulunmadığını gösterir. Bizansın alınmasından hemen sonra Türkler tarafından yapılan bazı bina ve çeşmelerde lâle motifinin görülmesi, lâle kültürünün İstanbula Türkler tarafından getirildiğini kanıtlamaktadır. Lâle süsleme motifi olarak 16–18. yüzyıllarda büyük bir önem kazanmıştır. Madeni eşya, kumaş, kitap ciltleri, tahta işleri, cam işleri, çiniler ve halılarda, karanfil, gül, sümbül ve zerren yanında, süsleme motifi olarak bilhassa lâle kullanılmıştır.

Evliya Çelebi 1630 yılında İstanbulda 80 çiçekçi dükkânı ve 300 çiçekçi esnafı bulunduğunu, İstanbul boğazi kenarlarındaki köşk ve yalıların bahçelerinin lâleler ve sümbüller ile süslenmiş olduğunu ve İstanbulun dört tarafında pek çok bağ ve bahçenin bulunduğunu kaydettikten sonra şöyle devam etmektedir: "Lâlezar mesiresi, Kâğıthane lâlesi adıyla meşhur olan çeşitli lâleler buradadır. Lâle vakti bu mesireyi görenin aklı perişan olur".

İstanbulda yüzyıllar boyu süren itinalı bir seçme sonucu elde edilen "Istanbul lâlesi" nin başlıca özelliği "Kadehi badem biçiminde, petalleri hançer şeklinde ve uç kısmı biz gibi ince ve sivri" olarak özetlenebilir. Osmanlı döneminde ancak yukardaki özelliklere sahip bir lâle bir öneme sahip idi. Diğer biçimdeki lâlelere "Kaba lâle" ismi verilirdi. İstanbulda elde edilen ve isimlendirilen 1500 kadar İstanbul lâlesi formu maalesef zaman ile tamamen kaybolmuştur. Bugün yalnız resimlerini gövdüğümüz ve yazmalarda özelliklerini okuduğumuz bu kültür formlarının, kısa zamanda yok olmalarını, çok az miktarda elde edilmiş ve yalnız meraklılar çevresinde kalmış olması ile açıklayabiliriz.

İmparator Ferdinand I. in elçisi olarak İstanbula gelen ve lâle'yi Avrupaya götürdüğü bilinen elçi Ogier Ghislain Busbecq'in Avrupaya İstanbulda elde edilen kültür formlarını değil, İstanbul pazarlarında satılan yabani lâle soğanlarından götürmüş olduğunu sanıyoruz. Çünkü 1560 yılında C. Gesner tarafından Türk lâlesi (*Tulipa turcarum*) ismi verilmiş olan lâle'nin İstanbul lâlesi ile bir şekil benzerliği bulun-mamaktadır.

Lâle devri (1700–1730) olarak isimlendirilen Sultan Ahmed III. ün damadı Nevşehirli Veziriazam Damat İbrahim Paşa döneminde lâle yetiştirme ve nadir lâle formlarına sahip olma merakı en yüksek noktasına erişmiş ve bu nedenle de lâle soğanı fiyatları çok yükselmiştir. Bu durumu önlemek amacıyla 1726 yılında lâle soğanı satış fiyatlarını saptayan bir fiyat listesi (Narh defteri) hazırlanmıştır. Bu listede en pahalı soğan "Nize-i rummani (Nar çiçeği mızrağı)" isimli lâleye ait olup 50 kuruş (7.5 altın) olarak saptanmıştır. Bu dönemde İstanbulda yetiştirilen lâle formları 1000 civarında olmakla beraber listede yalnız 239 lâle formunun ismi bulunmaktadır.

Lâle soğanlarının satışı, bugün de çiçek pazarı olarak kullanılan, Yeni cami (Eminönü) nin arkasındaki meydanda yapılıyordu. Bununla beraber bazı yetiştiriciler elde ettikleri formlara o kadar bağlı idiler ki, bu'nları sağlıklarında kimseye satmaya kıyamazlar, meraklılar bunları ancak mirasçılarından alabilirlerdi.

Bir halk hikayesine göre lâle Ferhad'in kanından meydana gelmiştir. Evliya Çelebi'nin kaydettiğine göre, Ferhad ile Şirin hikayesi, Amasyada geçer. Şirin'i alabilmek için Ferhad'dan Elma dağını delerek dağın arkasındaki suyu Amasyaya getirmesi istenir. İşe başlayan ve dağı delerek suyu kente getirmesine az bir zaman kala, Ferhad'a Şirin'in öldüğü haberi ulaştırılır. Bu habere çok üzülen Ferhad elindeki kazmayı havaya atar ve başını kazmanın altına tutar. Kazmanın başana düşmesi ile Ferhad ölür ve kanından "lâle" meydana gelir. Ferhad'in öldüğü yere "Kanlıpınar" denilir. Halen de Amasyanın Tokat yönünde Ferhad tarafından açıldığına inanılan bir su kanalı bulunmaktadır. Diğer taraftan Amasya bölgesinin *Tulipa* türleri bakımından Anadolunun en zengin bölgesi olması da dikkat çekicidir.

Yakın Doğu ve bu arada da bilhassa Anadolu, eskiden beri Avrupa bahçelerinde yetiştirilmekte olan birçok soğanlı ve yumrulu bitkinin vatanıdır. Bu bölge, Avrupa bahçelerine, *Colchicum byzantinum, Hyacinthus orientalis, Lilium candidum, Tulipa clusiana, T. gesneriana, Narcissus tazetta, Sternbergia lutea, Crocus sativus, Iris persica, I. reticulata* gibi birçok "klasik" soğanlı bitkileri vermiştir. Halen de Avrupa bahçelerini süslemek veya kolleksiyonları zenginleştirmek amacıyla her yıl bu bölgeden tonlarca yumru veya soğan toplanmaktadır.

Anadolu florası ve bitkilerine karşı olan ilgi oldukça eskidir. Bu alanda pek çok araştırma ve yayın yapılmıştır. Buna karşılık yalnız soğanlı ve yumrulu bitkileri kapsayan, bunların bir listesini, karakterlerini, yayılış alanlarını ve renkli resimlerini veren bir yayın bulunmamaktadır. Bu kitap yukarda belirtilen boşluğu doldurmak ve Türkiyenin soğanlı ve yumrulu bitkilerini daha iyi tanıtmak amacıyla hazırlanmıştır.

Kitabın hazırlanmasında 1950 yılından beri Anadoluda yapılan araştırma gezilerinde toplanan materyel (halen ISTE ve K herbaryumlarında bulunmaktadır), çekilen resimler ve bu alanda yapılan yayınlardan yararlanılmıştır.

Anadolunun yayla ve dağlarını gezerek yumrulu ve soğanlı bitkilerden kolleksiyonlar hazırlayan ve yayınlar yapan ve bu şekilde Anadolunun bitkilerinin tanınmasında katkısı bulunan ve bizim çalışmalarımızı da kolaylaştırmış olan araştırıcılara burada şükranlarımızı sunmak fırsatını bulduğumuz için kendimizi bahtiyar sayıyoruz. Bu kitap onların hatıralarına ithaf edilmiştir.

BIBLIOGRAPHY

1 Ahmed Kâmil: *Risale-i esami-lâle* (*Treatise on Tulip Names*) (AH1164/AD 1750), Hand-written, Ali Emiri Efendi Library, No. 158–171.
2 Ahmet Refik (Altınay): *İstanbul hayatı* (*Istanbul Life*), Istanbul, 1931.
3 Ahmet Refik (Altınay): *Lâle devri* (*Tulip epoch*), Ankara, 1937.
4 Ali Çelebi: *Süküfename-i musavver* (*Illustrated Flowers Book*) (AH 1078/AD 1667), Hand-written, Nuru Osmaniye Library, No. 3557–4077.
5 Aktepe, M.: Damat Ibrahim Paşa devrinde lâle (Tulips in Damat Ibrahim Paşa period) in *Tarih dergisi* 4: 85 (1952), 5: 85 (1953), 6: 23 (1954).
6 Aktepe, M.: Damat Ibrahim Paşa devrinde lâleye dair bir vesika (A document on tulips from Damat Ibrahim Paşa period), *Türkiyat Mecmuası* 11: 115 (1954).
7 Ar, M. S.: Etilerde bahar bayrami törenleri ('Spring festivals of the Hittites') in *Ankara Üniv. Dil ve Tarih-Coğrafya Fak. Der.* 2: 57 (1943).
8 Aslanoğlu Evyapan, G.: *Eski Türk bahçeleri ve özellikle eski Istanbul bahçeleri* ('The old Turkish gardens and specially old gardens of Istanbul'), Istanbul 1952.
9 Aşkî, Tabib Mehmed: *Miyarü'l ezhar* ('*Value of flowers*'), (AD 1800?) Hand-written, Ali Emiri Efendi Library, No. 167.
10 Atasoy, N.: Türklerde çiçek sevgisi ve san'atı ('Affection for flowers and floral art in the Turks') in *Türkiyemiz* 2 (3): 14 (1971).
11 Aulich, K.: *İstanbul florası-Monocotyledon kısmı* (*Flora of Istanbul-Monocotyledonae*), Istanbul, 1943.
12 Ayverdi, E. H.: *XVIII. asırda lâle* ('*Tulip in the 18th century*'), Istanbul, 1950.
13 Aznavour, M. G. V.: Note sur la flore des environs de Constantinople, in *Bull. Soc. Bot. France* 44: 164 (1897).
14 Aznavour, M. G. V.: Enumération d'espèces nouvelles pour la flore de Constantinople, accompagnée de notes sur quelques plantes peu connue ou insuffisament décrites qui se rencontrent à l'état spontané aux environs de cette ville, in *Mag. Bot. Lap.* 5: 156 (1906) and 10: 10 (1911).
15 Aznavour, M. G. V.: Etude sur l'herbier artistique Tchitouny, in *Mag. Bot. Lap.* 16: 1 (1917).
16 Aznavour, M. G. V.: Excursions botaniques du Dr B. V. D. Post au mont Ararat et aux environs de Rizé, in *Mag. Bot. Lap.* 17: 1 (1918).
17 Baker, A.: The cult of the Tulip in Turkey in *Jour. Roy. Hort. Soc.* 56: 234 (1931).
18 Baker, J. G.: *Handbook of the Irideae*, London 1892.
19 Balls, E. K.: Plant collecting in Turkey, in *Gard. Chron.* 98: 318, 370, 404, 440 (1935).
20 Bayramoğlu, F.: *Turkish glass art and Beykoz-ware*, Istanbul, 1976.
21 Baytop, T.: *Türkiyenin tıbbi ve zehirli bitkileri* (*Medicinal and poisonous plants of Turkey*), Istanbul, 1963.
22 Baytop, T.: The genus Tulipa in European Turkey in *J. Fac. Pharm. Istanbul* 11: 167 (1975).
23 Baytop, T.: The genus Colchicum in European Turkey in *J. Fac. Pharm. Istanbul* 12: 163 (1976).

24 Baytop, T.: Les tulipes de la Turquie occidentale–2. International symposium on the problems of Balkan flora and vegetation, 3–10 July 1978, Istanbul (1978).

25 Baytop, T. und Leep, H. J.: Zwei für die Türkei neue Arten der Gattung *Colchicum* (Liliaceae) in *J. Fac. Pharm. Istanbul* 13: 29 (1977).

26 Baytop, T., Mathew, B. and Brighton, C.: Four new taxa in Turkish *Crocus* (*Iridaceae*) in *Kew Bull*. 30: 241 (1975).

27 Baytop, T. et Özcöbek, G.: Recherches sur les alcaloides de *Colchicum chalcedonicum, micranthum, szovitsii* et *turcicum* in *J. Fac. Pharm. Istanbul* 6: 21 (1970).

28 Boissier, E.: *Flora orientalis* 5: 94–312, Genevae et Basileae, 1884.

29 Beck, F.: *Fritillaries*, London 1953.

30 Bowles, E. A.: *A Handbook of Narcissus*, London, 1934.

31 Bowles, E. A.: *A Handbook of Crocus and Colchicum for gardeners*, London, 1952.

32 Brighton, C. A.: Cytology of *Crocus olivieri* and its allies in *Kew Bull*. 31: 209 (1976).

33 Brighton, C. A., Mathew, B. and Marchant, C. J.: Chromosome counts in the genus *Crocus* (Iridaceae) in *Kew Bull*. 28: 451 (1973).

34 Burtt, B. L.: Two new species of *Colchicum* in *Kew Bull*. 5: 431 (1950).

35 Burtt, B. L.: Notes on *Colchicum* in *Notes Roy. Bot. Gard. Edin*. 21: 296 (1956).

36 Busbecq, O. G.: *The Turkish Letters of Ogier Ghiselin de Busbecq*, (trans. from the Latin by E. S. Foster), Oxford, 1927.

37 Ceram, C. W.: *Narrow pass, black mountain – The discovery of the Hittite Empire*, London, 1956.

38 Clusius, C.: *Rariorum plantarum historia*, Antverpiae, 1601.

39 Cordus Valerius: *Annotationes in Pedacii Dioscoridis Anazarbei de Materia Medica*, Venice, 1561.

40 Cullen, J. and Ratter, J. A.: Taxonomic and cytological notes on Turkish *Ornithogalum* in *Notes Roy. Bot. Gard. Edin*. 27 (3): 293 (1967).

41 Davis, P. H.: *Oncocyclus Irises in the Levant* in *Jour. Roy. Hort. Soc*. 72: 93 (1946).

42 Davis, P. H.: Fritillaries in the Eastern Mediterranean in *The Lily Year Book 1947*: 141 (1947).

43 Davis, P. H.: The spring flora of the Turkish Riviera in *Jour. Roy. Hort. Soc*. 82: 165 (1957).

44 Davis, P. H. and Henderson, D. M.: A revision of Turkish Lilies in *The Lily Year Book 1970*: 212 (1969).

45 Dayıgil, F.: Istanbul çinilerinde lâle (Tulips in Istanbul tiles) in *Vakıflar dergisi* 1: 8, 90 (1938) and 2: 223 (1942).

46 Dykes, W. R.: *The Genus Iris*, Cambridge, 1913.

47 Dykes, W. R.: *Handbook of Garden Irises*, London, 1924.

48 Dykes, W. R.: *Notes on Tulip Species*, London, 1930.

49 Eldem, S. H.: *Türk bahçeleri* ('*Turkish Gardens*'), Istanbul, 1976.

50 Ertem, H.: *Boğazköy metinlerine göre Hititler devri Anadolusunun florası* ('*Flora of Anatolia in Hittite age according to the Boğazköy texts*'), Ankara, 1974.

51 Evliyâ Çelebi: *Seyâhatnâme* ('*Travels book*') 2: 180, Istanbul, 1969.

52 Fedorov, A.: *Chromosome Number of Flowering Plants*, Koenigstein, 1974.

53 Feinbrun, N. A: A monographic study on the genus *Bellevalia* Lapeyr. in *Palestine Jour. Bot*. 1: 131, 336 (1939).

54 Feinbrun, N.: The genus *Colchicum* of Palestine and neighbouring countries in *Palestine Jour. Bot*. 6: 71 (1953).

55 Feinbrun, N.: The genus *Crocus* in Israel and neighbouring countries in *Kew Bull*. 12: 270 (1957).

56 Feinbrun, N.: Chromosome number and evolution in the genus *Colchicum* in *Evolution* 12: 173 (1958).

57 Feinbrun, N. and Stearn, W. T.: A revision of *Sternbergia* (Amaryllidaceae) in Palestine in *Bull. Res. Counc. Israel*, Sect. D: Botany 6D: 167 (1958).

58 Fedtschenko, B. A.: Species of flower bulbs of the Soviet Union in *Consp. Fl. Turkest.* (1913).

59 Fomin, A.: Des espèces nouvelles de *Muscari* et de *Tulipa* du Caucase in *Monit. Jard. Bot. Tiflis* 9: 11 (1908).

60 Foster, M.: *Bulbous Irises*, Roy. Hort. Soc., London, 1892.

61 Furse, P.: *Iris* in Turkey, Iran and Afghanistan in *The Iris Year Book, 1965*: 100 (1965) and *1968*: 61 (1968).

62 Furse, P.: Oncocyclus and Regelia Irises in Turkey, Iran and Afghanistan in *The Iris Year Book 1971*: 119 (1971).

63 Furse, P.: Iris reticulata section in *The Iris Year Book 1972*: 103 (1972).

64 Goulimis, C. N.: Les colchiques de Grèce et la repartition geographique du genre *Colchicum* in *Archia Tis Farmakeftikis (Athens)* No 1/2 and 3/4 (1956).

65 Grossheim, A. A.: *Flora Kavkaza* 2: 88, Baku (1940).

66 Gunther, R. T.: *The Greek Herbal of Dioscorides*, London, 1968.

67 Güner, A. and Peşmen, H.: Türkiye'nin Bazi *Iris* L. Türleri Üzerinde Taksonomik Bir Çalışma (A taxonomic investigation of the wild *Iris* of Turkey) in *Doğa Bilim Derg.*, Seri-A. 4 (3): 25 (1980).

68 Hall, A. D.: *The genus Tulipa*, Roy. Hort. Soc. London 1940.

69 Harvey, J. H.: Turkey as a source of garden plants in *Jour. Garden History Soc.* 4 (3): 21 (1976).

70 Hayek, A.: *Prodromus florae peninsulae balkanicae* 3: 18, Berlin (1933).

71 Herbert, W.: A history of the species of *Crocus* in *Jour. Hort. Soc. (London)* 2: 249 (1847).

72 Hoog, M. H.: On the origin of *Tulipa* in *Lilies and the other Liliaceae 1973*: 47 (1973).

73 Jefferson-Brown, M. J.: *Daffodils and Narcissi*, London, 1969.

74 Kalças, E. L.: Izmir 250 years ago: A famous Botanical Garden in *Jour. Garden Hist. Soc.* 6,2: 26 (1978).

75 Kollmann, F. and Shmida, A.: *Allium* species of Mt. Hermon, in *Israel Jour. Bot.* 26: 128 (1977).

75a Kollmann, F., Özhatay, N. and Koyuncu, M.: New *Allium* taxa from Turkey in *Notes R. B. G. Edin*, 41 (2): 245–267 (1983).

76 Komarov, V. L.: *Flora of the USSR*. 4, Engl. Ed., Jerusalem, 1968.

77 Kotschy, T.: *Reise in dem cilicischen Taurus über Tarus*, Gotha, 1858.

78 Koyuncu, M.: Türkiye florası için yeni *Allium* türleri, I. Sect. Allium, II. Sect. Codonoprasum (Some new species of Allium for Turkish flora I. Sect. Allium, II. Sect. Codonoprasum) in *Jour. Fac. Pharm. Ankara* 9: 45 and 54 (1979).

78a Koyuncu, M.: New and interesting Turkish records of *Allium* in *Notes R. B. G. Edin*. 38, 3: 417 (1980).

79 Koyuncu, M. and Kollmann, F.: Two new *Allium* species from Turkey in *Israel Jour. Bot.* 27: 90 (1978).

80 Krause, K.: Über türkische Gärten und Gartenwirtschaft in *Arch. f. Wirtschaftsforschung im Orient* 4: 443 (1913).

81 Krause, K.: *Ankaranın floru (Zur Flora von Ankara)*, Ankara, 1934.

82 Lâlezari, Şeyh Mehmed: *Mizanü'l ezhar (The habit of flowers)* (AH 1115/AD 1703), Hand-written, Ali Emiri Efendi Library, No. 163.

83 Levier, E.: Les Tulipes de l'Europe in *Bull. Soc. Sci. Nat. Neuchâtel* 14: 201 (1884).

84 Leure, E.: L'origine des Tulipes de Savoie et de l'Italie in *Archives Ital. Biol.* 5: 48 (1884).

85 Louis, H.: Das Natürliche Pflanzenkleid Anatoliens in *Georg. Abhandl.*, Heft 12 (1939).

85a Malyer, H.: (In Turkish) A chronological study of the geophytes of the family

Iridaceae from the Diyarbakır area, in *Doğa Bilim Derg.*, Seri-A, 6 (1): 17 (1982).

86 Marais, W.: Notes on *Tulipa* (Liliaceae) in *Kew Bull.* 35 (2): 257 (1980).

87 Marchant, A. and Mathew, B.: *An alphabetical table of the genus Iris*, The British Iris Soc., London, 1974.

88 Mathew, B.: Turkey and South-East Europe, 1965, part I in *Jour. Roy. Hort. Soc.* 91 (8): 334 and part 2 in 91 (9): 383 (1966).

89 Mathew, B.: *Dwarf Bulbs*, Batsford, London, 1973.

90 Mathew, B.: *Crocus olivieri* and its allies (*Iridaceae*) in *Kew Bull.* 31 (2): 201 (1976).

91 Mathew, B.: *Larger Bulbs*, Batsford, London, 1978.

91a Mathew, B.: *The Iris*, Batsford, London, 1981.

91b Mathew, B.: *The Crocus*, Batsford, London, 1982.

92 Mathew, B. and Baytop, T.: Some observations on Turkish *Crocus* in *Notes Roy. Bot. Gard. Edin.* 35 (1): 61 (1976).

93 Mathew, B. and Baytop, T.: A new white *Sternbergia* in *The Garden* 104: 302 (1979).

94 Mathew, B., Brighton, C. A. and Baytop, T.: Taxonomic and cytological notes on Asiatic *Crocus* in *Notes Roy. Bot. Gard. Edin.* 37 (3): 469 (1979).

95 Maw, G.: *A monograph of genus Crocus*, London, 1886.

96 Mehmed Remzi: *Gonce-i lâlezar-ı bağ-ı kadim*, (AH 1115/AD 1703), Ali Emiri Efendi Library, No. 157-172.

97 Mouterde, P.: *Nouvelle flore du Liban et de la Syrie* 1: 203-322, Beyrouth (1966).

98 Murray, W. S.: The introduction of the Tulip and the Tulipomania in *Jour. Roy. Hort. Soc.* 35: 18 (1910).

99 Nabelek, F.: Iter Turcico-Persicum, pars IV, *Publications de la Faculté des Sciences de l'Université Masaryk* No. 105, Brno (1929).

100 Özhatay, N.: Trakya bolgesi ve Istanbul çevresi *Alliaceae* familyası üzurinde taksonomik, sitolojik ve palinolojik araştırmalar ('Taxonomical, cytological and palynological studies on the family Alliaceae in European Turkey and around Istanbul') *Dissertation*, Univ. of Istanbul (1977).

100a Özyurt, S.: (In Turkish) A taxonomic investigation on the geophytes of the family Liliaceae from N.E. Anatolia in Atatürk *Univ. Fen Fak. Derg.* 1 (2): 17 (1981).

101 Polunin, O.: Some bulbs of Middle East, I and II in *Gard. Chron.* 145: 125 and 172 (1959).

102 Polunin, O.: Kurdistan-Iraq for bulbs, I and II, in *Quart. Bull. Alp. Gard. Soc.* 28: 40 and 210 (1960).

103 Post, A. and Post, B. V. D.: *La Flore du Bosphore et des environs*, Istanbul, 1950.

104 Post, G. and Dinsmore, J. E.: *Flora of Syria, Palestine and Sinai*, 2: 583, Beirut, 1933.

105 Randolph, L. F.: The geographic distribution of European and Eastern Mediterranean species of bearded *Iris* in *The Iris Year Book 35*, London (1955).

106 Rechinger, K. H.: *Enumeratio florae Constantinopolitanae*, 57, Dahlem, 1938.

107 Rechinger, K. H.: Flora Aegaeae in *Denkschriften d. Akad. d. Wiss,* 105 (1943).

108 Rechinger, K. H.: Florae Aegaeae supplementum in *Phyton* 1: 194 (1949).

109 Redouté, P. J.: *Les Liliacées*, Paris, 1802-1816.

110 Regel, C.: Vegetationszonen und Vegetationsstufen in der Türkei in *Fedde Rep. Beih.* 138: 230 (1959).

111 Rix, E. M.: Three new Fritillarias from Eastern Turkey in *Notes Roy. Bot. Gard. Edin.* 31: 125 (1971).

112 Rix, E. M.: Notes on *Fritillaria* (*Liliaceae*) in the Eastern Mediterranean region, I and II, in *Kew Bull.* 29: 633 (1974).

113 Rix, E. M.: Notes on *Fritillaria* (*Liliaceae*), in the Eastern Mediterranean region, III in *Kew Bull.* 30: 153 (1975).

114 Rix, E. M.: *Fritillaria* L. (*Liliaceae*) in Iran in *Iran Jour. Bot.* 1: 75 (1977).

115 Rodionenko, G. I.: *The genus Iris*, Moscow, 1961.

116 Sauer, W. und Leep, H. J.: Karyologische Untersuchungen an anatolischen und südost-europäischen Zwergiris-Sippen: *Iris attica, I. mellita* und *I. reichenbachii* (Iridaceae) in *Pl. Syst. Evol.* 131: 81 (1979).

117 Sauer, W. und Stegmeier, R.: Beiträge zur Kenntnis südost-europäischer und anatolischer Bart-Iris-Arten (Iridaceae) in *Ber. Deutsch. Bot. Ges.* 92: 663 (1979).

118 Saunders, D. E.: *Cyclamen in the Wild and Cultivation*, The Alpine Gard. Soc., London, 1975.

119 Schefer, C.: *Journal d'Antoine Galland pendant son séjour à Constantinople (1672–1673)*, Paris, 1881.

120 Schischkin, B.: Contributiones ad floram Armeniae Turcicae, I in *Ber. d. Tomsker Staatsuniv.* 80: 409 (1929).

121 Schwarz, O.: Additamentum ad florulam Lydiae, I in *Fedde Rep.* 36: 74 (1934).

122 Schwarz, O.: Tentative key to the wild species of *Galanthus* L. in *Bull. Alp. Gard. Soc.* 31: 131 (1963).

123 Siehe, W.: Die gruppe 'Juno' der kleinasiatischen *Iris* Arten in *Allg. Bot. Zeitschrift* 11(7–8): 7(1905).

124 Stearn, W. T.: Notes on the genus *Allium* in the old World in *Herbertia* 11: 11 (1946).

125 Stefanov, B.: Monographie der Gattung *Colchicum* L. in *Sbornik. Bulg. Akad. Nauk* 22 (1926).

126 Stern, F. C.: *Snowdrops and Snowflakes, a study of the genera Galanthus and Leucojum*, London, 1956.

127 Synge, P. M.: Some *Iris* in Turkey and Persia in *The Iris Year Book, 44*, London (1961).

128 Takhtajan, A. L. and Fedorov, A. M.: *Flora Erevana*, Leningrad, 1972.

129 Tanker, N. and Kurucu, S.: Türkiyede doğal olarak yetişen bazı *Allium* (Soğan) türleri üzerinde sitotaksonomik araştırmalar ('Cytotaxonomical researches on some species of *Allium* naturally growing in Turkey') in *J. Fac. Pharm. Ankara* 9: 64 (1979).

130 Tchihatcheff, P.: *Flore de l'Asie Mineure 2*: 515, Paris, 1860.

131 Turrill, W. B.: The genus *Fritillaria* in the Balkan peninsula and Asia Minor in *Jour. Roy. Hort. Soc.* 62: 329 (1937).

132 Tutin, T. G. et al.: *Flora Europaea*, Vol. 5, Cambridge, 1980.

133 Ubeydi, Mehmet bin Ahmet: *Netâyicü'l ezhar* ('*Effect of flowers*') (AH 1110/AD 1701), Hand-written, Ali Emiri Efendi Library, No. 162.

134 Ünver, S.: The history of Tulips in Turkey in *The Daffodil and Tulip Year Book 1969*, 46, London (1968).

135 Ünver, S.: The Narcissus in the history of flowers in Turkey in *The Daffodil and Tulip Year Book 1968*, 67 (1967).

136 Walter, H.: Vegetations gliederung Anatoliens in *Flora* 143: 295 (1956).

137 Warburton, B.: *The World of Irises*, Amer. Iris Soc. Wichita, Kansas, 1978.

138 Webb, D. A.: The flora of European Turkey in *Proc. Roy. Irish Acad.* 65B: 1 (1966).

139 Vvedensky, A. L. and Fedtschenko. B. A.: *Species of Wild Flower Bulbs of the Soviet Union*, Moscow, 1935.

140 Wendelbo. P.: The genus Allium in *The Lily Year Book* 30: 86 (1967).

141 Wendelbo, P.: Amaryllidaceae, in Rechinger, K. H., *Flora Iranica* No. 67, Graz (1970).

142 Wendelbo, P.: Alliaceae, in Rechinger, K. H.: *Flora Iranica* No. 76, Graz (1971).

143 Wendelbo, P.: *Tulips and Irises of Iran*, Tehran, 1977.

143a Notes on *Hyacinthus* and *Bellevalia* (Liliaceae) in Turkey and Iran, in *Notes Roy. Bot. Gard. Edin.* 38 (3): 423 (1980).

144 Wendelbo, P. and Mathew, B.: Iridaceae in Rechinger, K. H.: *Flora Iranica* No. 112, Graz (1976).

145 Werckmeister, P.: *Catalogus Iridis, 1967*, Deutsche Iris- und Liliengesellschaft e. V., Leonberg bei Stuttgart, 1967.

146 *Defter-i Lâlezâr-ı Istanbul* ('*Book of Tulip gardens in Istanbul*') (AH 1138/AD1726), ms., Ali Emiri Efendi Library, No. 157–164.

147 *Musavver sümbülname* ('*Illustrated Hyacinths book*') (AH 1149/AD 1737), ms., Topkapı Saray Library, No. H-413.

148 *Sûrnâme-i Humâyun* ('*The book of festivities of Sultan Murat III.*') (AH 990/AD 1582), ms., Topkapı Saray Library, No. H-1344.

149 *Revnak-ı bostan* (*Beauty of the Garden*) (translated by A. Özkök), Ankara, 1967.

TURKISH INDEX

GENERAL INDEX

Accepted botanical names are given in italics. Synonyms are given in roman type. Main
page references are given in italics. Figures in bold are illustration numbers.

pulchellus **27**, *35*, 111
reticulatus subsp. *hittiticus* **20**, *33*
reticulatus subsp. *reticulatus 33*
sativus **28**, 29, *35*, 109, 111
scharojanii **29**, *36*
sieheanus 15, *33*
smyrnensis *32*
speciosus subsp. *ilgazensis 36*
speciosus subsp. *speciosus 36*, 111
speciosus subsp. *xantholaimos 36*
suworowianus = subsp. of *C. kotschyanus*
  35
tauri = subsp. of *C. biflorus* 8, *31*
tournefortii 16
vallicola **30**, 35, *36*
vallicola var. suworowianus *35*
vitellinus 32, *33*
zonatus = *C. kotschyanus* subsp.
  kotschyanus 34
Cyclamen 111
  cilicium 111
  coum 111
  persicum 111
Danae 108
  racemosa 108
Dracunculus 111
  vulgaris 111
Eranthis 111
  cilicica 8, 23, 111
Eremurus 23, 108
  cappadocicus 108
  spectabilis 108
Erythronium 50
  dens-canis 50
Fritillaria 75
  acmopetala subsp. *acmopetala* 75, **82**, 111
  acmopetala subsp. *wendelboi* 75
  aintabensis 78
  alburyana 75, **83**
  alfredae subsp. *alfredae 76*
  alfredae subsp. *glaucoviridis* 76, 80, **84**
  alfredae subsp. *platyptera 76*
  armena 76, *77*
  assyriaca subsp. *assyriaca 76*
  assyriaca subsp. *melananthera 76*
  aurea 76, **85**
  bithynica 76
  canaliculata 76
  carduchorum 79
  carica subsp. *carica 77*
  carica subsp. *serpenticola 77*
  caucasica 77, **86**
  cilicico-taurica, 10, *76*
  citrina 76
  crassifolia subsp. *crassifolia* 77, 78
  crassifolia subsp. *hakkarensis 77*
  crassifolia subsp. *kurdica* 77, **87**
  dasyphylla 76
  elwesii 9, *77*
  erzurumica 75
  fleischeriana 78
  foliosa 77
  forbesii 9, *78*
  glaucoviridis 76
  grossheimiana 77
  haradjianii 76
  hermonis subsp. *hermonis 78*
  hermonis subsp. *amana* 78, **88**

imperialis *78*, 111
karadaghensis 77
kurdica 13, *77*
latakiensis *78*
latifolia *78*, **89**
lutea *78*
lycia *75*
michailovskyi *79*, **90**
minima *79*
minuta *79*, **91**
nobilis *78*, **89**
olivieri *13*
ophioglossifolia 15, *77*
persica *79*, **92**, 111
pinardii *79*, **93**
pineticola *76*
platyptera = subsp. of *F. alfredae* 76
pontica *79*, 111
schliemannii *76*
sibthorpiana *79*, **94**
sieheana = *F. elwesii* 10, *77*
straussii 7, *80*
stribrnyi *80*
syriaca 15, *79*
subalpina *80*
uva-vulpis *80*
viridiflora *80*
wanensis *77*
whittallii 17, *80*
zagrica *80*
Gagea *80*
  ambylopetala *81*
  anisanthos *82*
  arvensis *84*
  bithynica *81*
  bohemica *81*
  boissieri *84*
  bulbifera *81*
  chanae *83*
  chlorantha *81*
  chrysantha *81*, *82*
  confusa *82*
  damascena *81*
  dubia *83*
  fibrosa *82*
  fistulosa *82*
  foliosa *82*
  gageoides *82*
  glacialis 10, *82*
  granatellii *83*
  graeca *81*, *82*
  helenae *83*
  joannis *83*
  juliae *83*
  linearifolia *83*
  liotardii *82*
  luteoides *82*, *83*
  peduncularis *83*
  pinardii *83*
  pratensis *83*
  reticulata *83*, *84*
  sintenisii *83*
  smyrnaea *81*
  syriaca *83*
  szovitsii *81*
  taurica *84*
  tenera *81*
  tenuifolia *82*